WOMEN
UNDERWATER

Jill Heinerth & Reneé Power

Published by:

Heinerth Productions Inc.
5989 NE County Road 340
High Springs, FL 32643 USA

First published 2014
Copyright © Jill Heinerth
Photography, illustrations and text
by Jill Heinerth and Reneé Power

This manual is not intended to be used as a substitute for proper dive training. SCUBA diving is a dangerous sport and training should only be conducted under the safe supervision of an active diving instructor until you are fully qualified and then only in conditions and circumstances which are as good or better than the conditions in which you were trained. Careful risk assessment, continuing education and skills practice may lessen your likelihood of an accident but are never a guarantee for complete safety.

Cover Photo: Reneé Power enjoys the crystal clear waters of a North Florida Spring. Photo: by Jill Heinerth with equipment support from Santi Diving and Halcyon.

Book design Heinerth Productions Inc.
www.IntoThePlanet.com
Printed in the USA
ISBN 978-1-940944-01-2

Acknowledgments

In 1979, Susan Bangasser and Jeanne Bear Sleeper published the first book to specifically reach women divers. In 1992, Ella Jean Morgan and Erin O'Neill published *When Women Dive*. They were way ahead of their time. All inaugural inductees into the Women Divers Hall of Fame, they were true pioneers in our industry. We are proud to build on the foundation of these remarkable women.

In the late 1990s, my dear friend Patty Mortara and I were lamenting the lack of resources for and connections between the very few female technical divers around the world. With Velora Peacock, we started an organization called Cardea 2000, in the hopes that we could better connect women tec divers around the world by the turn of the century. Patty and I started a magazine called *Women Underwater* in order to further that cause. Edited and printed in small numbers the quarterly was mailed out around the world until we ran out of money to do it. We shared stories about expeditions, gear and resources with our growing community of women technical divers. I knew one day I would dust off the concept and this book is very much the result of that desire.

Patty Mortara and Jill Heinerth, editing slides at National Geographic Headquarters in 1999.

Co-author, Reneé Power and I would like to thank the many people, organizations and manufacturers who assisted this project with loans and gifts of equipment, donation of charters and volunteer support. Specifically, we would like to thank Dr. Maida Taylor for incredible support and research, and Santi Diving, who provided Reneé with a drysuit when she really needed it and who continue to support my work generously. We would also like to thank: Amigos Dive Center, Aqualung, Ken Charlesworth, Cobalt Coast Dive Resort, DiveRite, DiveSangha, Divetech and InDepth Watersports in Grand Cayman, Halcyon, Bob and Sylvia Ledbetter, Light & Motion, Peter Skop Industries (PSI), Rick's Dive 'N Travel, SCUBA-Blog.com, Seminole SCUBA, and Suunto.

This book was carefully proofed and edited by Kristine Rae Olmsted. It is an enormous task and we truly appreciate her talent, support and guidance in bringing this to fruition.

- Jill Heinerth

Table of Contents

About the Authors

A pioneering underwater explorer and filmmaker, Jill Heinerth has dived deeper into caves than any woman in history. Jill's photography has been featured in prominent international publications. Recognizing a lifetime devoted to water advocacy, Jill was awarded the *Wyland Icon* and *Sea Hero of the Year* awards. In recognition of her lifetime achievement, Jill was presented with the inaugural *Medal for Exploration*. Established by the Royal Canadian Geographical Society, the medal recognizes the pursuit of excellence by an outstanding explorer. Her *We Are Water Project* combines documentary filmmaking, live presentations and social media to spread water literacy on a global scale. Her website IntoThePlanet.com is the home for the *Women Underwater* blog, store and educational resources.

Reneé is a volunteer with the Cambrian Foundation, an aquatic research organization. Since 1994 she has participated in dozens of underwater research projects and public education outreach efforts. Alongside the Cambrian Foundation dive team, she has engaged in original exploration surveying thousands of feet in Mexico and Florida caves.

Reneé is an active PADI Master Instructor. Her technical training includes Full Cave, Trimix and Prism Topaz Rebreather. Reneé is a Disabled Diver International instructor and has served in the Deptherapy Program with wounded military veterans. Her favorite students are the ones she helps overcome the greatest challenges, obstacles and fears. Reneé's company, Dive by Design, offers a personal approach to dive instruction. She can be reached at DiveByDesign.com.

Introduction

In the era of women's rights and feminism, many of us seek to diminish the differences between genders and instead fight for true equality. As such, I have been questioned about why I would want to separate women and men in the field of diving. I've received a few angry emails suggesting that this effort sets back attempts at gaining equality. Recently, I got a Facebook note from a man who thought the notion of a women's specific book was patently ridiculous. In this case, my husband wanted to answer, "I guess you've never had to worry about having your period in a wetsuit!" (I've got a really cool, and incredibly proud husband).

This book and its accompanying website seek to address much more than information about women's specific health issues. Truthfully, our industry is only just beginning to recognize that women need distinct solutions for equipment rather than something that is simply made small and pink. In careers, women still struggle to be considered capable of participating in traditionally male-dominated professions. On dive boats, women are still frequently treated with insensitivity, prejudice and even harassment. Clearly these are unique issues that women face in the underwater world.

This book aims to reach out to women to help find their place in the diving community. With detailed guidance on equipment, medical issues and social factors, we have also included inspiring stories and advice from mentors who have forged remarkable careers in underwater fields. Our hope is to provide a solid reference and inspiration for women to feel included and capable of pursuing their unique path in diving.

We hope you'll enjoy reading and continue to follow our blog at IntoThePlanet.com.

- *Jill Heinerth*

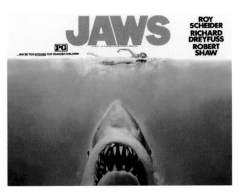

The Evolution of Dive Equipment

In 1949, Desco Equipment and Supply Company published a catalog of diving equipment that included two pages of instructions for use. Within those two pages, customers were offered a condensed class that encompassed gear as well as dive tables and safety warnings. Some of the gear consisted of items such as nose plugs, hard hats and "swim-tails," now known as fins. Their 1955 catalogue depicted brave hard hat divers exploring the ocean while sexy bikini-clad women water-skied above them. It was a long way from where we are today. People ordered their gear from catalogs and had to locate a hospital or fire station that would fill their tanks. Divers were self taught in basements and clubhouses without a real sense of community. Today, we are at a critical junction in the evolution of our sport. We're either moving our industry forward or slipping back into those early dark ages.

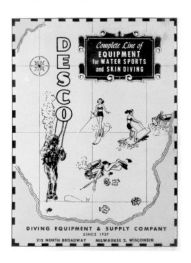

In the last ten years, our shopping preferences have gradually shifted toward online retailers that offer exceptional pricing, variety and availability. Having once owned a dive store, this author can tell you it was extremely difficult to compete on price alone. In the following chapter we describe specific issues, fit and options for various dive gear. You'll read our repeated advice to try on equipment before making a big purchase. Your local dive shop will be able to help in this process but will not be able to carry everything you find on the Internet. At the same time, they are able to offer you local air fills, good service, instruction and a sense of community. These services are not likely to pay their rent or compressor bills, so we implore you to consider working *with* your local retailer in a partnership that keeps them viable in the future. They might give you a chance to try on a potential new suit and make a test dive to narrow down features that help you make a choice in BCDs. But rather than running back to a computer to place your order, ask the retailer to help you get the gear you need. Be prepared to wait a bit for a delivery rather than looking for instant gratification through Amazon Prime. Take note of the services the dive shop will be offering you and consider the added value that they will bring to your diving experience.

The focus of this chapter is not to school you in all the basics of dive gear, but rather to explore features, fit and suggestions that are specific to women divers. For each section, the authors offer personal perspectives, opinions and unique solutions. Representing two ends of the size spectrum from petite to lanky, we face unique issues with our gear. We've been told to wear children's fins and men's wetsuits to find the right fit and have had to get creative to make things work.

Recreational Gear

Recreational diving equipment encompasses all the basic gear needed to make single tank no stop dives in water less than 130 feet/40 meters deep. Although some divers use sidemount gear at the recreational level, we have included that equipment in the technical category.

Masks

Your dive mask is your window to the world. It may be the first piece of equipment you buy and one of the most critical pieces for ensuring optimized vision, comfortable breathing and a positive experience.

General Features

Diving masks come in single and double paned versions. A single lens mask offers a wide field of vision and looks terrific in photos, but a double lens mask offers you more options for replacing the lenses with a personal prescription. Although you might like the appearance of a particular mask, it is critical that you choose a mask that fits you properly and provides optimal vision.

Offering a wide field of vision, a single lens mask (above) offers the best unobstructed view of your eyes in photographs. Photo: Courtesy of Aqualung. PrescriptionDive-Masks.com offers fully customized prescription masks (below). Photo: Gene Page

Fit/Sizing

Masks are fabricated in many different varieties, though a particular style will likely only be offered in one size. In a few cases, a mask style is manufactured in a standard and narrow fit. The size of the mask is reflected in several ways including the internal volume of the mask, the relative size of the frame and lens(es) and the actual silicone skirt. You'll have to try on several masks before you find one that fits you well. The skirt should seal well around your face without being too wide. Some women have narrow faces and may have trouble finding a good fit. Attention should also be focused on the nose pocket to ensure that it is not oversized. If you live in a cold area, be sure you can equalize and pinch your nose with your choice of gloves.

Materials

Soft silicone skirts should be comfortable and form fitting. Some skirts are made with a harder material that does not conform well to the curves of our faces. If you wear a hood when you dive, you might want to try on the hood with your mask to check to see if the hood distorts the mask skirt in any way.

Special Considerations

Beyond fit, experiment with the operation of the mask straps. Are you able to easily adjust the strap buckles with your chosen gloves? Does the strap roll and entangle your hair? Does the strap sit comfortably on the back of your head in a way that won't slide off?

Men's Versus Women's Styles

Some manufacturers offer masks that are specifically designed for women. These masks tend to be lower in volume and sized for narrower faces. Nose pockets are generally smaller. Feminine styling and colors are often added in addition to special features that are specifically geared for women. These may include special strap and buckle options that prevent hair entanglements and more supple skirt materials.

Jill's Opinions

I have always been a fan of neoprene mask straps. I immediately replace my silicone strap with a neoprene version that adheres with Velcro. I try to find a strap that won't leave any of the stiff side of the Velcro exposed since that tends to grab my hair and

scratch my skin. I have never cared for decorative neoprene strap covers. I find that they create a gap (between the adjustable buckles and the strap cover) that entangles my shoulder length hair.

As I have aged, it has become increasingly difficult for me to read my gauges. I started by purchasing small glue-in "readers" that magnified the view in the lower left corner of my left lens. As my vision worsened, I have graduated to full-blown bifocals. Without them, I am unable to read my gauges or focus my camera. Off-the-shelf readers are made for some brands of masks, but I prefer finding a perfectly fitted mask and then having prescriptions made for me. I turned to *PrescriptionDiveMasks.com* to make lenses that fit my favorite mask. I mail them my mask and indicate how high I would like the bifocals to extend up the lens and the mask is returned as a proper magnifying bifocal mask.

Reneé's Opinions

I prefer a silicone strap because I feel it is more secure on my hood. I have short hair so there's no chance of it getting pulled. When my hair was longer I sought out a neoprene strap with Velcro closures and loved it. Like Jill, I don't care for the neoprene strap covers. My experience is that the strap can fold and get twisted under the cover and they offer no protection from hair getting pulled at the adjustment points.

Reneé Power diving in Grand Cayman.
Photo: Jill Heinerth

Aging and vision changes go hand in hand. I love using a very low volume mask. I use small, hardly noticeable readers in the lower part of the lenses. I dive with a distance contact lens in my right eye and wear my computers on my left arm. With this integration I can see my gauges, camera, students and the boat.

Black is my preference for a skirt color. I find it's much easier to see my camera screen, gauges and just about everything else. I have tried clear silicone skirted masks and I found myself squinting on sunny days in the open water. I remember during my very first night dive in my PADI Advanced Open Water course I wore a huge pink mask with side windows that were supposed to enhance peripheral vision and let in more light. It did indeed. However, the undulating aquatic plant life in the periphery seemed like monsters in the darkness. I was quite miserable and determined to never night dive again! With a black skirt and no side windows I'm able to stay more visually focused and less distracted since my peripheral vision is blocked. Recently I have discovered the AquaLung Linea mask. It is designed especially for women using supple silicone and an ergonomic design. It is lower volume and now comes in a black skirt. I just sent this off for readers and now it is my "go to" mask. Well done AquaLung!

Fins

Fins are the engine that drive us through the water. As such, they should fit our bodies and our type of diving, yet few fins have been specifically designed for women. In fact, significant differences exist in knee alignment and muscle activation between women and men. Lengthy studies have been conducted for sports such as soccer, yet physiologists have never turned their attention to diving and how fins might be better designed for women. In a study used to aid in the prevention of sport's injuries, it was determined that male soccer players activate the hip flexors in their kicking leg and the hip abductors in their supporting leg more than females. In the kicking leg, men generated almost four times as much hip flexor activation as females (123 percent in males compared to 34 percent in females). Males also generated significantly greater activation of other critical muscles in the butt, hip and thigh.[1] A study of biomechanics in men and women divers could net important revelations about better designs to suit our feminine bodies.

Fins are an integral part of balancing your body to result in good trim. The weight and buoyancy characteristics of your fins are are extremely important for optimizing results. Photo : Jill Heinerth

[1] Robert H. Brophy, Sherry Backus, Andrew P. Kraszewski, Barbara C. Steele, Yan Ma, Daniel Osei, and Riley J. Williams. Differences Between Sexes in Lower Extremity Alignment and Muscle Activation During Soccer Kick. *Journal of Bone and Joint Surgery,* 2010; 92: 2050-2058 DOI: 10.2106/JBJS.I.01547

General Features

There are several features to consider when selecting a fin including blade proportions, foot pocket size and dimension, strap style and relative buoyancy of the fin.

Fit/Sizing

Fit considerations should include examination of the blade size in proportion to your body. If you are a small woman, then a large blade may cause unwanted fatigue. On the other hand, a larger woman may find a petite blade to be inadequate for powering her body through the water. Some woman become frustrated by the fact that a small foot pocket is not available in a "real" fin and is only found in children's sized or lower quality fins. If your foot is diminutive, you may want to wear heavy/thick soled booties that enlarge your foot and allow it to be accommodated in a larger, more substantial fin. Another solution involves cutting up an old wetsuit to create a small neoprene sleeve that goes over the arch of your foot on the outside of your boot. It adds to the overall thickness of your foot and creates a cushioned sleeve that fills out the fin pocket, thus keeping the fins more stable on your feet.

Sherwood Fusion fins with spring straps. Photo: Courtesy of Peter Skop Industries.

You may have to put on your fins while standing on the back of a rocking boat. Consider how you will put them on and whether you can put them on with our help. Photo: Jill Heinerth

Materials

Your fin is not just a propulsion device but is also a piece of the puzzle that helps you find perfect horizontal trim in the water. Like a seesaw in a playground, your body has a pivot point or center of balance. The fins on the end of your feet can drastically affect your overall position in the water by either floating or sinking your feet. If your fins are too heavy, they may feel like boat anchors dragging your feet through the muck and if they are too light, they may hinder good kicking ability or throw off your trim. Some fins are constructed with materials that are positively buoyant while others are negative. If you dive a neoprene drysuit, then you may need to source a heavy fin made of rubber that sinks your feet. If your feet tend to drag along the bottom, then a lightweight, positively buoyant material may work better for you.

The modern materials used in fin construction offer unique qualities beyond relative durability. Some engineered materials "snap" back after initial thrust is applied by the diver. These features are difficult to assess in the comfort of a dive shop. If available, take a test dive or borrow your friend's fins to select the best possible model for your body size and gear configuration.

Special Considerations

Fin straps are produced in different styles including numerous types of buckles and mechanisms. Some fins are also assembled with spring straps that fit a variety of suits without the need for adjustment. You need to be able to bend over in a thick wetsuit or drysuit and adjust fins and remove and replace them independently. Look for mechanisms that make that easy. If you travel a lot you may end up buying a second set of fins that is lightweight for warm climates and plane travel.

Men's Versus Women's Styles

As mentioned earlier, few companies have designed fins that are specific for women. Aqualung offers fins that have features beyond feminine styling. The foot pocket's design, width, compounds and sizing are dedicated specifically to women's feet resulting in greater comfort, better sizing and an easier kick.

Jill's Opinions

I believe there is no perfect fin for all women in all styles of diving. In Florida, I appreciate having fins that are very light in the water. They help me keep my feet up off the floor of the caves that I dive within. Yet, when I head north for diving at home in Canada, I prefer having fins with a little more negative buoyancy. Wearing more layers of undergarments, my legs get a little lighter. Having heavier fins in this case, keeps my legs in an optimized trim.

The women of the Sedna EPIC Expedition show off their fins as they cross the Arctic Circle near Greenland. Photo: Courtesy www.SednaEpic.com - Jill Heinerth

I'm a tall woman with a large foot. I wear a ladies size ten shoe, yet I find that most fin pockets are unnecessarily wide, designed specifically to accommodate men's feet. Some spring straps are also made for very large feet. My foot slides laterally in these fins, wasting my energy. Sometimes I can sort this lateral movement out with a heavier, thick-soled boot and some fins offer a bit of a tread inside the foot pocket to prevent my foot from moving around. Small details are very important since I often face high flow within caves or difficult currents when I am forced to push a large camera through the water.

Reneé's Opinions

I'm Jill's polar opposite at 5 feet (152 cm) tall. My very petite foot, size 5.5 , seems darling; but it has been my lifelong nemesis. It's hard enough finding wetsuit or drysuit boots to fit. Once I find them I have to search for fins that are acceptable for the application. Like Jill, I have more than one set of fins; I currently have about 6 pairs. My old drysuit was constructed of ridiculously heavy neoprene with size 6 neoprene boots with thick insoles inside to make them fit better. The suit was positively buoyant and the boots were thick so I needed XL Jet Fins. That was just too much for me to push around so I used a fin with a slightly larger fin pocket that was still a bit negative. I don't have the oversize problem at all with my new Santi drysuit, designed specifically for women. In a wetsuit I found a lighter fin that fits perfectly with standard women's booties. My DiveRite XT fins fit both my AquaLung Ellie Ergo boots and the boots on my Santi Ladies First drysuit. Win!

Snorkels

Even the lowly snorkel deserves some special examination. If you enjoy snorkeling it may be a *very* important piece of equipment to you, offering you the chance to swim comfortably without developing mouth sores or spending the entire swim coughing and hacking.

General Features and Fit

The most important general concern regarding a snorkel is finding one with a mouthpiece that fits comfortably and securely. Some brands offer two sizes of replaceable mouthpieces that make your experience on top of the water comfortable and dry. A replaceable mouthpiece also means you

This Sherwood snorkel features a corrugated barrel to optimize comfortable fit of the mouthpiece. Photo: Jill Heinerth

can select one that works well if you have special needs such as preventing the onset of painful temporomandibular joint disorders (TMJ). The volume of lower purge mechanisms should be sized so that you can easily clear them with a normal breath. Rotation on the lower barrel may also help you find a relaxed and comfortable fit.

If you snorkel exclusively without SCUBA, you might consider a swimmer's racing snorkel. These front mounted designs from Croatia are very comfortable at high speed when you create a "bow wave" that might otherwise swamp a traditional snorkel. Photo: Jill Heinerth

Special Considerations

The attachment of the snorkel to the mask might be a consideration for women with long hair. A hard plastic fitting may become entangled in your hair. A soft neoprene retainer may work better.

Jill's Opinions

I prefer snorkels with easy purge systems and rotating, corrugated barrels that give me the ultimate comfort to swim for a long time. I use a figure-eight shaped neoprene snorkel keeper to lessen entanglement with my hair. I can quickly slide the keeper and snorkel off my mask without too much of a challenge. This is important to me since most of my dives (in caves) do not require a snorkel. I don't want to struggle while removing and replacing a keeper every time I head to the caves.

I like using folding or collapsible snorkels for ocean tec diving. Snorkels conflict with my breathing loop on my rebreather, but I don't want to be in the ocean without one. A pocket snorkel solves that problem, though I challenge manufacturers to come up with a better design that functions well and can be easily stowed away.

Reneé's Opinions

I am a big fan of snorkels. It's required when I teach recreational diving and I've grown accustomed to wearing one. Like Jill, I want to have a snorkel when ocean diving. I prefer a simple design with a basic splash guard at the top and a mouthpiece with a flexible tube. I like a smaller diameter snorkel because my lungs are small. It's hard for me to clear the larger bore snorkels. For open water tec diving I agree it just gets in the way. I second the challenge for a better collapsible snorkel design. Then people would really have no excuse not to carry one.

Weights

Weight systems are as varied as the types of diving that they are designed to support. Comfortable weighting should provide you with ample ballast for correct neutral buoyancy underwater, be easy to ditch to allow you to gain proper positive buoyancy on the surface and should be carried in such a way that they help you achieve good horizontal trim that protects the environment and puts you in an effective and streamlined position to swim. Additionally, weight systems should not cause lower back pain or make equipment too heavy to lift or carry-on the surface. They should be easily adjustable and able to be removed and replaced in the water or on the boat. That's a big list, but safety and comfort can be optimized with careful consideration of the points above.

Integrated shoulder weights can be woven into a technical diver's harness to shift trim, bringing the shoulders down and the feet up. This is often helpful for rebreather divers. Photo: Jill Heinerth

General Features

There are several common ways that people wear lead weights. They include:

- Weight belts— a quick released belt supports either lead block weights or shot lead pouches.

- Integrated ballast weights— Some buoyancy control devices (BCDs) are equipped with pockets in the back that accommodate lead blocks or lead shot pouches. This lead is generally not ditchable by the diver, but is intended to help trim you into position or accommodate overflow from the ditchable pockets.

- Integrated weight pockets— Some BCDs are equipped with quick-release pockets that are easily dropped with one hand in the event of an emergency. These proprietary devices are brand-specific and operate in differing ways.

- Trim weights— In some cases, divers weave lead weight blocks into their harness or BCD straps, usually in the region of the shoulder. These trim weights help pivot a diver whose feet are dragging into a more streamlined position in the water. These are generally not able to be dumped in an emergency.

- Drop weights – A small weight of 4 lbs/2 kg or less is rigged with a clip so that a diver may use it to compensate for the first atmosphere of pressure. In cases where it is feasible, the weight is removed and clipped to the line or left in a safe place for retrieval at the end of a dive. The weight is re-clipped to the diver for the safety or decompression stop. Drop weights are most commonly used by technical and cave divers.

- Ankle Weights— If you have a neoprene dry suit, thick wetsuit boots or naturally buoyant feet, then you may need some small ankle weights. I suggest experimenting with negatively buoyant fins first, but if your legs are still rising up, try ankle weights. Some are very long and shift around small ankles. They need to be fairly snug and immovable to be comfortable when swimming without cutting off circulation. Look for models that offer adjustment in length and an easy buckle that can be operated with your gloves if applicable.

- Weight harnesses— A weight harness marries a traditional weight belt with suspenders that better distribute the weight over the body. Some are designed to be either partly or wholly ditchable. Beware of harnesses with straps that cut into your breasts. It can be very uncomfortable.

Pocket weight belts are equipped to contain comfortable soft lead shot bags. Photo: Jill Heinerth

Fit/Sizing

A well fitted weight system should be reasonably comfortable with enough of it ditchable for emergencies, allowing you to easily achieve positive buoyancy. Divers in cold water wearing heavy undergarments wear the most weight, where a tropical diver in a skin may not need any at all. The cold water diver will also be wearing heavy gloves for thermal protection and should ensure that everything in their system of choice is operable with gloves.

Special Considerations

Most women have a higher body fat content than men. Unfortunately, body fat generally translates into increased buoyancy and a greater need for lead ballast. If you choose to integrate all your weights into BCD pockets, consider carrying the weight separately from the SCUBA unit when on shore. Lugging the mass of equipment and installed weights

may be more than you wish to handle on an uneven dock or rocky shoreline. Get a sturdy han-
dled bag(s) for your weights and carry them on a
separate trip. If you must walk with your BCD and
weights for a long distance, consider this in your
choice of weight system and BCD. Some manufacturers offer BCDs that are similar to hiker's
backpacks, offering good weight distribution and
comfortable ergonomics for long walks.

*Quick release weight pockets can be useful.
You can remove weight before carrying the
BCD and tank. Photo: Jill Heinerth*

If you are on a boat, you will be switching your
BCD from an empty tank to a full one for the sec-
ond dive of the day. If all your weights are integrated, it might be tough to lift the BCD up
and over to the next tank. If some of the weights are easy to remove, this task will be
much easier.

Men's Versus Women's Styles

Men have a tough time with weight belts since they don't have the same hourglass
shape that women generally do. A weight belt tends to sit ideally on our shapely hips and
stay there. There is no reason to rule out this simple solution. However, if you choose a
standard weight belt, consider getting a belt with shot pockets or rounded coated weights.
Squared edges on lead block will be uncomfortable for anyone wearing a thin suit and
may even cause bruising.

Jill's Opinions

Integrated weight pockets may be useful in some situations but I only like using them if
the weight is minimal. Putting a large mass in those pockets makes the unit ungainly on
the shore and tough to pick up. It also makes it front heavy on a boat, allowing it to tip
over if not secured in place. Women with shorter arms may find that the bulk of integrated
pockets are difficult to reach around. Weight pockets may squeeze into the capacity of
the accessory pockets or make it difficult to reach something that has been clipped onto a
lower D-ring. I like using a standard weight belt in many cases. It is easy to ditch in an
emergency, easy to carry-on its own and easy to pass up to a Divemaster on a boat. I
generally prefer to keep my positive buoyancy (BCD) separate from my negative buoyancy (weight belt).

Reneé's Opinions

For me, weight distribution is key. Like the old saying goes, "don't put all your eggs in
one basket." I like the idea of being able to ditch little bits of weight at a time in case I
ever had to do an emergency buoyant ascent. Trim can be nicely adjusted with weight
placement. I do most of my diving in the year round 72°F/21°C Florida springs, so I currently utilize a 7 mm wetsuit or drysuit. My preference is to disperse the weights in the
trim pockets, the quick release BCD pockets and a weight belt. My arms are a bit short
(like a T-Rex dinosaur) and I find it difficult to reach around loaded BCD weight pockets

when teaching weight belt removal and replacement. I dive a small BCD, and loaded weight pockets can make me feel a bit bulky as well. Steel cylinders are generally heavier which assists with weight distribution. Each type of cylinder has its own unique buoyancy specification so I always take that into consideration for weighting at the end of my dive.

Weight belts are becoming a thing of the past in some areas. Most manufacturers design BCDs with an integrated weight system. Many divers find the weight integration convenient, but convenience comes with a price. Valuable storage space may be sacrificed to accommodate weight pockets that result in increased torso bulk. Whichever method you choose, remember to be sure the weights can be easily accessed and released at any time. Get creative and play with the weighting to get your trim in a nice horizontal position.

Women's BCDs are designed to fit shorter torsos while accommodating women's breasts. A chest strap helps prevent the shoulder straps from slipping down. Photo: Jill Heinerth

Buoyancy Control Devices (BCD)

NATO commissioned an extensive study in 2002 to compare the body proportions of men and women from North America, The Netherlands and Italy for the purpose of designing safety apparel for personnel. The results of their work demonstrate a strong separation between men and women and determined that scaled-down equipment did not adequately meet the needs of women and actually created safety issues that could jeopardize military operations. Just looking at hip size alone, they realized that the design of flight suits, cold water immersion suits, anti-g suits and other protective suits needed to be specifically redesigned to fit women.[2]

Women have a lower center of gravity. We have shorter torsos, longer legs and wider hips. Men have longer torsos and a lot of weight in their chests. If you find a man and woman of equal height and place them side by side, it's likely that her legs will be longer than his and his torso will be longer than hers. Or, if you find a man who is a little taller than a woman, you will likely find that their legs will be of equal length.

Women's shoulders are generally narrower and slope downward from the neck. Shoulder straps need to be shorter, contoured and narrower since our waistline is higher than a man's. Our necks are smaller too, and obviously, we have breasts that need to be accommodated into the design specificities.

---

[2] Gender Differences in NATO Anthropometry and the Implication for Protective Equipment, Adam M. Fullenkamp, Kathleen Robinette, Hein A.M. Daanen, Air Force Research Laboratory/Biomechanics Branch, USA and TNO Defense, Security and Safety Business Unit Human Factors, Soesterberg, The Netherlands.

General Features

Women's-specific BCDs have received quite a lot of attention in the last decade. Beyond styling, the relative size of women versus men has been addressed by many manufacturers. Rather than being an afterthought, BCDs have been designed in several styles that accommodate a variety of needs. There are several features to consider when fitting a BCD. Try BCDs on with and without a tank attached so that you know how it will feel when you have to walk from the car to the boat.

- Shoulders— Make sure the BCD does not feel like it is either cutting into your neck or falling off your shoulders. It should sit squarely and securely on your shoulders with adequate padding to stay in place. The shoulder straps need to be contoured and adjustable and should allow for adaptation to different exposure protection. Quick release shoulders may make it easier for you to take the unit off after diving. Swiveling shoulders may better accommodate larger breast sizes.

- Chest— Women come in all sizes. Some BCDs integrate a bra-like crossover system that secures the BCD without needing to use a chest strap. This may add to insulation value if it is made of neoprene. If a chest strap is used to secure the front, then check if it is adjustable in length and vertical position. Ideally you should be able to move it higher or lower on your sternum. You don't want it to cut into your breasts, neck or block the drysuit inflation valve if you use one.

Swiveling mechanisms on the shoulder straps may create greater comfort by angling the straps away from the breasts (above). BCD jackets may be equipped with many additional features such as knife or light holders, streamlined inflation devices or accessory pockets (below). Photos: Jill Heinerth

- Waist— Cummerbund waists are comfortable but ensure they don't block the utility of a quick release weight belt. With short torsos, we don't have a lot of space beneath our breasts. The cummerbund should sit squarely on the waist and stop the BCD from riding upward when inflated on the surface. Oftentimes a quick release buckle offers a second layer of security on top of the cummerbund waist strap.

- Back— As mentioned, the torso of a woman's BCD should be shorter than a unisex version. The back should be well padded for comfort.

- Weight pockets—If your BCD of choice contains weight pockets, are you able to reach and drop the weights? Can you load them standing or sitting on a boat? Can they be accidentally released when you reach for other equipment? Try the BCD with weights installed to ensure you can still reach all other features. Try the pockets with hard and soft weights to see which will be easier to load.

Ensure the closure on the cam band is easy for you to operate and securely holds the size of tank you want to use. Some Velcro closures may not accommodate small tanks properly. Photo: Jill Heinerth

• Accessory pockets— Can you reach these pockets if you decide to use the weight pockets? Can you operate the closure with gloved hands? Does your hand fit in the pocket and permit you to remove and replace accessory items?

• Tank straps— Are these straps located in such a way that they will accommodate the size of tank you prefer? In some cases the straps are too far apart and will not fit shorter tanks. In other cases, the Velcro closures on the straps are only capable of fitting standard diameter tanks and not narrow, smaller versions.

• Inflation device and air dump— Many styles of inflators and dump valves are installed on BCDs. Some are completely integrated into the body of the BCD. If you choose this style consider purchasing the appropriate low pressure inflator hose as a back up if it is an odd size or connection. Ensure you can operate the inflation and dump mechanism in your choice of exposure protection.

You may consider using a streamlined inflator system that doubles as an octopus.

• Lift Capacity— Some small women's BCDs have negligible lift capacity. Make sure you will have adequate lift when you are wearing a heavy tank and cold weather gear if applicable. In cold water, we often wear substantial weight to sink a dry suit but we want to be sure the BCD matches appropriately with lift when needed.

Fit/Sizing

Fit and comfort are very personal. A dive shop salesperson may be able to point out features, but ultimately you will need to choose the system that fits you the best. Oftentimes, a store will not have the correct size or model to fit you perfectly. This is not the time to compromise and take something off the shelf that is close. Be patient. Find the unit that is right for you and have the shop order in the correct size if necessary. Women frequently buy BCDs that are too large for them. The harness should be snug to prevent the unit from shifting underwater.

Styles

BCDs are built in many styles. A jacket style wraps like a coat, offering stability on the surface, but more overall bulk. A BCD with lift in the back can sometimes pitch you forward on the surface, but hangs comfortably horizontal underwater. This style will have more open "real estate" or available space in the front for clipping off accessory items. Some recreational divers choose to use a backplate/wings combination that will be covered in the technical section later in the book.

Special Considerations

A BCD is a significant investment. Don't get too emotionally attached to a BCD until you have evaluated all features for you specifically. You may wish to look several years down the road to consider the type of diving you might be interested in doing in the future. Taking future classes and environments into consideration now may affect your purchase decision. A recreational BCD is rarely capable of carrying you into tech diving, but a single tank tech diving setup can be appropriate for a new recreational diver too.

Men's and women's BCDs are designed with unique fit characteristics. Be sure to try a woman-specific BCD before making a purchasing decision. You may be surprised at the additional comfort and features available to you. Photo: Courtesy of AquaLung

Men's Versus Women's Styles

There is simply no comparison between a BCD that has been designed specifically for a woman's shape and one designed for general gender-neutral consumption. Thankfully we have arrived to a time when women's BCDs are not just small and pink. They are not simply a down-sized afterthought. They actually fit. Unisex BCDs often squeeze a woman's breasts, fall off the shoulders, rise up around a woman's ears when inflated on the surface, have waistbands that fall down around our hips and are simply uncomfortable for our curves.

Jill's Opinions

Your ultimate goal is to find a solution that offers safety, comfort and stability. You want to prevent the unit from "riding up" when it is inflated on the surface. It should feel snug and stable without moving around. Out of the water, you want a system that keeps your tank close to your center of gravity and transfers the weight to your hips so you can easily stand up and walk as if you were wearing a hiker's backpack. That means that my perfect fit won't be yours. This piece of equipment may be the toughest to fit, but once you have found it, you'll want to dive the same BCD for the rest of your life.

I dislike Velcro anywhere close to my head and neck. Shoulder epaulettes that secure with Velcro either scratch me or end up entangled in my hair. Velcro may also destroy a wetsuit or skin. I prefer a smooth, velvety surface inside the BCD so that if I wear it with minimal protection, it will be comfortable on my skin. I might not dive without a suit, but I am very likely to wear the BCD from the boat to the car when I am wearing only a swim suit or sort sleeved shirt.

Reneé's Opinions

I definitely don't have a lot of space. I wear a small BCD and it can get cluttered easily. If I'm not careful, I can feel like my gear is controlling me instead of the other way around so I find other places to stow accessory items than the seemingly obvious D-ring that beckons for something to be clipped to it. If I start clipping lights, a slate or other accessories on my BCD it's almost a guarantee that my alternate air source deployment will be hindered. My open water BCD has a little pocket to stuff the alternate air source hose into. This works great with increasingly popular braided hoses. (These hoses have a slick surface compared to a standard hose).

Suunto staff enjoying dives off Southern France. Photo: Jill Heinerth

Generally a woman's BCD tends to be smaller than a man's. It may or may not have less accessory attachment points and pockets but one thing is for sure; a woman's dive gear can get way too cluttered. Because we are often smaller than men, there is usually less available space to put things. It's important to have the items we need both accessible and positioned so that they don't obstruct deployment of needed equipment. In the open water diver class, students learn that the alternate air source should be stored in the triangular area formed by the diver's chin and the angles of the ribcage. Very little if anything else should be located here. It is critical to keep the primary regulator and alternate air source clear of other equipment so they may be freely deployed in an emergency. My preference is the back inflated harness style BCD when "fun" diving. When teaching students in the open water I'll use my recreational BCD that is more bulky, but offers the support and position I need on the surface.

Rash guards offer abrasion protection as well as sun coverage. Photo: Courtesy of AquaLung

Exposure Protection— Skins

Skins are Lycra, polypro-type fabric or 1 mm thin neoprene suits that may be worn alone in warm water or underneath a suit to add insulation. Lycra undersuits make it easy to slide on a form-fitting neoprene wetsuit. A new class of thin fabric suits such as Lavacore and Sharkskin offer real insulation in addition to abrasion protection and sun coverage. Most skins contribute very little to no positive buoyancy.

General Features

It is desirable to wear a skin or rash guard rather than just a bathing suit. Sun and marine life protection are important. One manufacturer designs skins with light knee pads, spine and lower back padding. The question you need to ask yourself is whether you want some additional insulation and abrasion protection in addition to the above. Skins come in all price points that reflect their features.

Fit/Sizing

Skins should be form fitting. If they do not conform to your body, they will drag in the water. Look for solid seam construction since you will be stretching and tugging at the material to get dressed and to remove it after your dive. Skins are available in onesies, tops, pants, shorts, hooded vests and many other models. Look for flat seams that will be comfortable against your skin. Select a heavy-weight fabric that offers sun protection factor.

Jill's Opinions

I find that a Lycra skin is very handy for quickly sliding into a snug wetsuit. It also offers sun protection if I pull down my wetsuit to my waist between dives. Sometimes I use Lavacore products on their own for very warm water dives and a Lavacore or Sharkskin hooded vest to increase the thermal protection of a wetsuit. I find that a variety of different pieces can be a handy compliment for all my water sports. On a morning swim, I like to wear some coverage beyond my bathing suit and let's face it, at my age, I don't really enjoy running around in a bathing suit at any time!

Reneé's favorite rash guard helps spread the word about a terrific diving resource found at: www.ScubaBlog.com. Photo: Jill Heinerth

Reneé's Opinions

It is a rare day that I don a wetsuit without some sort of skin underneath. I'm very cold natured so I like to layer. I start with my Aeroskin that offers a tiny bit of warmth along with spine and lower back padding. Then comes the Lavacore hooded vest and finally my 3, 5 or 7 mm wetsuit. If I have to be in the water for an extended amount of time in a wetsuit, I'll don my Thermolution heated top that really takes the edge off. Also I like a skin to protect from random annoying jellyfish stings. My newest favorite exposure protection in warmer water or for layering under a wetsuit is the Sharkskin. I use their Chillproof long pants, vest and hooded long sleeve top. These products also reduce the amount of weight I need to wear since they don't add buoyancy. Another win!

Exposure Protection— Wetsuits

It is important to note that wetsuits offer some of their thermal protection by trapping a layer of water against our skin and preventing flushing of fresh cold water into the suit. As such, they need to fit the contours of our body well. Wetsuits come in varying thicknesses from 1 mm to 8 mm neoprene and every imaginable price point. Your choice of wetsuit will depend on fit and your budget. It is all but impossible to select a wetsuit online without trying it on first. Dive shops are the best source for suits since you can verify the fit first hand.

Beyond thermal protection, wetsuits need to offer comfort, flexibility and fit for myriad activities supporting and beyond your diving plans. Photo: Jacqueline Windh

General Features

You need to make a good investment in thermal protection. Fit is important, but so is construction quality. Low cost suits are often made with inferior stitching and poor quality neoprene that gets crushed flat the first time you dive. Bad seams unravel and leak. Many women appreciate anatomically bent arms and legs, curvy cuts and features such as arm or leg zips. Integrated hoods, internal wrist, ankle and zipper gaskets and dams improve warmth. Supple, stretchy material eases the dressing process as does a smooth interior finish. Varied thickness of neoprene in a suit can improve fit and lessen water flow-through. Knee and elbow pads add to durability and longevity of the suit without compromising thermal capacity.

The term semi-dry suit refers to a suit style that fits very well, has welded seams and has additional dams or seals at the wrists, ankles and neck. The suit is designed to minimize or almost eliminate water ingress and the seams are fully sealed and waterproof. Truthfully, a good top end wetsuit should do the same as suits that are dubbed semi-dry.

Akona Quantum Stretch neoprene is not only flexible but also constructed in an earth-friendly manner. The four-way stretch suits are offered in a wide range of women's sizes. Photo: Jill Heinerth

Fit/Sizing

Your wetsuit should be skin tight without compromising circulation. Once you are dressed, you should ensure that you still have adequate range of motion to reach all of your equipment with relative ease. Not all brands will have a solution that works for you. Custom suits are available from a few specialty manufacturers, but they are generally pricey. If you decide to go custom, be very careful to follow measurement directions precisely in order to get the best fit.

If you buy a men's suit, you may have areas that are too snug and others that are baggy. The roomy parts permit water flow that will leave you chilled. Extra long legs or arms have to be either bunched or folded over and neither of those solutions is very preferable.

Materials

Not all neoprene is made alike, nor is the seam construction. Look for high quality fabrics that can be easily slipped over wet skin. Carefully examine the seam construction to ensure the seams don't leak and can take ample stretching without breaking threads. Supple, stretchy materials are much easier to put on than stiff ones, but check that the quality is such that it will survive the number of dives you intend to do. Cheap neoprene may get crushed into a wrinkled mess at depth and never recover its appearance or thermal capacity.

Men's Versus Women's Styles

Fortunately many women's specific suits are available from numerous manufacturers. You still may find a better fit in a man's suit depending on your body morphology. Try on as many different models as possible and then choose a suit with ample thickness or layers. Most people underestimate the thickness of suit they will require to stay warm. Ever water as warm as 82°F/28°C will eventually leave you cold.

Jill's Opinions

Wetsuits are notorious for odd sizing. I have personally fit anything from a size 8 to a women's XL plus in the same week. Don't be ashamed if you find yourself in something with a huge size tag on it. Cut off the tag so it doesn't haunt you at night! I have found that suit sizing is often associated closely with the size of the citizens in the manufacturer's country. I have tried suits with tiny short legs, with shoulders that were so tight I couldn't get the zipper up and crotches that hung down around my knees.

I like to wear suits that are flexible and very thick. The first year that I lived in Grand Cayman I did all my dives in a bikini. By the third year I realized that a 5 mm suit kept me warm all day. If I am warm and comfortable, I want to be in the water! If I am cold, I am simply not happy.

My favorite accessory is a hooded vest. That keeps water from running in and out at the neck. I think it adds a significant amount of thermal protection without reducing my mobility in any way. I dislike Velcro on suits as much as I dislike it on BCDs. Velcro at the neck always snags my hair and irritates the skin on my neck. It also grabs Lycra and the suit threads and frays anything it touches. Recently Aqualung Europe began experimenting with a magnetic closure to eliminate all Velcro. Great feature!

Reneé's Opinions

Hey Jill, where can I find the suit you tried with the tiny short legs? That's right; another nemesis. It doesn't matter the suit is marketed as "short." It's still going to be too long for me. It's not the suit's fault. My challenge to manufacturers is to make suits for women with many more sizing options. It seems that as the weight increases on the sizing charts, so does the length. Some women are short and squatty (that might be me) so please make suits that fit a wide variety of women. I wear a size 8-10 Bare wetsuit but it is far too long in the legs and arms. I have to fold the ankle and wrist Glideskin seals back which defeats the purpose. I love wearing a 3 mm wetsuit when diving in the warmer Caribbean waters. I dive mostly in the Florida Springs inviting a thicker wetsuit. I also love my hooded vest. Even if I don't pull the hood on, it keeps the back of my neck warm since I don't like to fasten the Velcro neck strap on the wetsuit.

Exposure Protection— Swimsuits

There is not too much special guidance to offer on swimsuits except to consider things such as chlorine resistance and UV protection. Consider minimizing bulky items such as a padded bra in the suit since it takes a long time to dry and leaves wet "boob marks" on your t-shirt when you put it on over your wet swimsuit. A two piece tankini or similar model makes it is easier to get changed in public under a towel. Modest coverage tops can easily be worn with shorts before and after diving. You can choose to change into dry shorts without changing tops.

Exposure Protection— Drysuits

Today's drysuit selection is substantial. Numerous materials, styles and a custom fit make it possible to satisfy most women who can afford to make a bit of an investment.

General Features and Fit

There are several types of suits available. In general, you can choose between models made of neoprene, crushed neoprene and various trilaminate or fabric materials. There are numerous features or styles that are worthy of consideration:

Drysuits offer the best solution for comfort. It is generally agreed that if women divers are warm, they will continue diving but if they are uncomfortable, they will find another sport. Photo: Jill Heinerth

• Zipper Placement— Rear zip suits are generally more form fitting than front zip but are not as convenient for self-donning. Diagonal front zippers are easy to zip for some yet small women might find that these zippers wrap around their body too far making it impossible to dress without help.

• Seal Type— Neck and wrist seals may be constructed of neoprene, latex or silicone. A woman's head to neck ratio is very different from a man's. Women's necks are generally smaller than men's in proportion to their head size. That means it might be challenging to get a thick neoprene neck seal over your face and when you do, it might be too big for your neck. Once they are on, they are definitely warm. Latex seals are easier to get into and silicone even stretchier. Latex rubber may dry rot in a warm environment and all seals should to be treated with care so you don't accidentally rip them when getting dressed. If you have long nails, this can be an issue.

- Seal Construction— Neoprene and latex seals are sometimes offered in user-replaceable models. These seals can be replaced quickly on a ring system that is integrated into the suit. The problem with a replaceable neck seal is that the neck ring may be very wide, built universally to fit a man's head. That means it is wide enough to limit your reach across your chest. Even for a tall woman with long arms, this ring can limit range of motion or dig into collar bones. The diving harness generally sits on top of the ring, making it even more uncomfortable. Some manufacturers are addressing this issue and the similar problem associated with large wrist rings. The newest drysuit designs offer oval rings that are lower profile for the wrist and a smaller version of a neck ring.

- Boots— Boots may be offered as neoprene socks that come with overboots or built in booties with soles of various designs. It can be challenging to properly fit a woman's small or narrow foot. Even overboots are tough to find in small sizes. Many of us prefer ordering our suits with form fitting neoprene socks. If you can't get an overboot in your size, then order an oversized Converse high top sneaker or oversized standard wetsuit boot with a heavy sole. The goal is to limit problematic air spaces in the foot and lower leg that can create issues with trim. If the lower leg traps a lot of air, an inexpensive pair of leg gaiters will help control the situation.

Santi's Ladies First is the first drysuit to boast a completely women's-specific design with a wide number of standard sizes, a semi-custom option and a full custom measurement option for divers. The zipper has been reversed from most self-donning suits so that it does not interfere with the left arm dump valve. Photo: Jill Heinerth (above) Courtesy of Santi Diving (below)

In expeditionary environments, there is no room for less than top quality exposure protection. Photo: Courtesy of www.SednaEpic.com - Jill Heinerth

• Custom Measurements— Custom suits are carefully constructed using over 20 different measurements. Check with the manufacturer to find out whether their system will create a truly custom fit for you or whether they will be using your measurements to find the best selection of a variety of pattern pieces to fit together. Understanding how they construct a custom suit may help you determine whether it is worth the investment in customization. Follow measuring instructions very carefully and be sure to involve a professional or friend to do it for you. It is not possible to self-measure accurately.

Special Considerations

Buoyancy and drag are important things to think about with various styles of suits. Neoprene suits are quite thick and buoyant, yet they are cozy even if they flood. Crushed neoprene reduces some of the bulk and positive buoyancy while retaining warmth. Membrane/trilaminate suits have no inherent thermal capacity when flooded but they are slick, streamlined and lightweight for travel. You can choose undergarments that offer good thermal integrity when wet.

When you try on a suit, be prepared to get hot. Dress in the full compliment of undergarments so you can determine if you will be able to reach valves, do up your zipper or bend over. There is no way to judge a suit effectively without dressing fully.

You may be asked to choose between a snug fit and loose cut. If you plan to wear diapers/incontinence pads for long dives, keep them in mind when selecting a suit or getting a custom measurement. Diapers increase bulk around the hips and waist significantly.

Men's Versus Women's Styles

There is simply no comparison between suits for different genders. Women's-specific cuts take into account the unique shape and proportions of our bodies. Custom measured suits are even better.

Jill's Opinions

I've owned easily a dozen different drysuits during my career and found that they have improved significantly over the years. Construction has improved and so has fit. I own one unisex suit that fits me reasonably well, but have found superior construction and fit in custom suits. I dive in all temperatures of water, but have moved away from neoprene and crushed neoprene finding better waterproofing in fabric suits. Trilaminate/membrane suits allow me to choose the right underwear for the particular dive. I request a custom suit to be slightly oversized to retain capacity for heavy undergarments and let the compression of water streamline the suit when I am wearing less. Santi's new "Ladies First" line is the first suit and accessory line that is specifically featured for women. They have added many women's specific features including careful placement of the inflation valve to accommodate women's breasts, reinforced and padded crotch gusset, coned wrist seals in smaller sizes and tailoring to fit women's curves. They are serious suits for serious divers, not a remodeled bottom end men's suit with a splash of color.

Reneé's Opinions

I am currently on my fifth custom drysuit. The first, back in the early 90s was a nylon suit. It kept me warm but leaked and gave a lot of resistance. My next suit was neoprene. I loved it and yet it eventually aged beyond repair and I had to let it go. The challenge for me with neoprene is that it is very, very buoyant and heavy out of the water. The stretchy neoprene wrist and neck seals are nice and the neoprene boots tend to be warm, yet a buoyant suit means wearing more weight to sink. It gets to be too much to manage on the surface or underwater. One of the women divers I know and respect (yes, Jill) suggested that I try a non-neoprene drysuit. She told me of the Santi Ladies First drysuit about to be released. I caved (pun intended) and felt remarkably less buoyant, have more range of motion, I can don it myself and I'm even warmer. The first time I walked to the water with my backmount doubles on I recall thinking I had forgotten something because I felt so light and could move easily. I can't lie, it felt weird! It seemed I had forgotten my drysuit when in fact I hadn't. What I did leave behind was a whole lot of bulky neoprene.

Reneé Power smiles after her first dive in her new Ladies First suit from Santi Diving. Photo: Jill Heinerth

Exposure Protection — Undergarments

Undergarments for drysuits come in every thickness and style you can imagine. From Thinsulate or Merino lightweight underwear to heavy Polartec one piece under suits, there is an appropriate style and thermal capacity for every water temperature and activity.

Undersuits should offer women's specific features such as "trap door" openings to allow ladies the comfort of using the toilet without completely undressing in a cold environment. Photo: Courtesy Santi Diving

General Features and Materials

Pants, tops, vests and one piece undersuits are all offered for drysuit diving. You'll want to find something of an appropriate thickness that has a slick outside surface that makes it easy to slip inside a dry suit. Undergarments should be constructed of technical materials that retain thermal capacity when wet and that wick moisture away from the diver. It is likely that you will sweat in an undergarment before getting in the water. You don't want the sweat to chill you before you even go diving.

The layer of material next to your skin should have flat seams that stay comfortable when compressed by a drysuit. Photo: Courtesy of Lavacore.

Unless you are diving in extremely warm water, avoid cotton next to your skin. It will trap moisture and enhance the cooling effect. Modern performance wicking materials are a far better choice beneath your drysuit. Photo: Robert McClellan

Never put cotton next to your skin. It will hold chilling moisture against your body. If you prefer natural fibers over synthetic, investigate Merino wool which has excellent thermal capacity and wicking capability.

Some manufacturers have recently released incompressible undergarments. These unusual suits feel a little stiff on the surface, but will trap a warm layer of air against your body throughout your dive and possible decompression. The garment tends to have a thick panel on the front of the torso where compression is the greatest in horizontal trim. These suits are very warm but require a little more weight to effectively sink. Some of these undergarments are built into suits and stay with the suit rather than the diver. They are still removable for cleaning, and make dressing very fast.

Fit/Sizing

Stock unisex undersuits may not fit most women. The length of the legs and the height of the waist are often built for men. Women may find a better fit by selecting two-piece sets or women's specific cuts. Santi offers custom measured undergarments including specially designed and fitted women's undersuits.

Men's Versus Women's Styles

Men's one piece undergarments often zip from the top and the bottom for the sake of convenient urination. This can be an important feature for a woman who uses a P-valve in her suit. Santi offers a two-way zipper that unzips all around from the neck down to the crotch and around the back and now a special trap door version for women. This can be extremely handy for privacy on boats and in the field in very cold environments. You can unzip adequately to allow you to sit down on the toilet without taking off your entire suit. Pulling your panties aside, you can use the toilet without getting undressed.

Jill's Opinions

Several years ago, I got my first pair of Santi custom measured undergarments. It never occurred to me how important this was. I was restricted in all my previous custom measured drysuits because the crotch hung too low or the shoulders were too tight in my undersuit. The drysuit fit was fine, but with ill-fitting undergarments I was hog tied inside my suit. I will never purchase another drysuit without well fitted custom undergarments again. I often wear a light layer of Merino or Polypro beneath my one piece jumpsuit. Most of the sweat is contained in the under layer that can be washed often. I don't like to wash my jumpsuit as much, figuring that will extend its overall lifespan.

Reneé's Opinions

I've never had custom undergarments until very recently. Thus, the arms and legs are almost always to long. I've enjoyed wearing two piece undergarments by Fourth Element. They are available in a variety of thicknesses. My new Santi Ladies First drysuit has custom undergarments that enable my drysuit to be donned with ease and the arms and legs don't have to be rolled up! And....there's a "trap door" for using the restroom so I don't have to take the whole suit down. I love that in colder weather!

Exposure Protection— Hoods

The hood on your wet or drysuit is an important part of the thermal envelope as well as abrasion or bump protection.

General Features

Hoods come in various styles from Lycra caps to Lavacore technical fabric hoods and full 7-10 mm cold weather hoods. The length of the neck skirt impacts thermal protection as does the thickness of the neoprene. Many divers own more than one hood for different temperatures of water and it is okay to double up and wear two hoods when it is really cold.

Fit/Sizing

As mentioned earlier, a woman's head to neck ratio is greater than a man's. In other words, the man's head is closer in size to his neck than a woman's. We tend to have a tougher time getting

Two layered hoods may be better than one for warmth and extra features. Photo: Mike Gerzevitz

a hood over our head if it fits well on the neck region. Some manufacturers have equipped their hoods with expansion zippers to help women get them over their head. Supple neoprene is also very helpful.

Soft neoprene against the face area will promote a seal with the skin and reduce flushing. Many hood openings are made small so they can be carefully trimmed to fit a diver's face perfectly. If you feel like the hood is clamping your jaw shut, it may merely be in need of a little trimming.

Jill's Opinions

When I wear a wetsuit, I prefer wearing a hooded vest to reduce flushing around the neck region. For drysuits, I try to find a hood with the best fit around my neck, or with a completely custom fit for perfection. If the hood is loose on the neck, it will be very cold. Dry suits with neck dams that permit the hood to be tucked under a lip are warmer than those without.

Reneé's Opinions

I always wear a hood, usually neoprene. I may even put on a second lightweight hood for extra exposure protection. This creates a little space for storage of small items.

When it comes to boots, you might find that skipping the zippers actually offers more warmth and better fit. Photo: Jill Heinerth

Exposure Protection— Boots/Socks

Dive boots have been completely unisex until recently. Aqualung was the first to offer women's specific dive boots. They even designed these boots to pair well with the foot pocket of their women's specific fins. There are numerous features that can improve the fit and comfort of dive boots.

General Features and Fit

Boots are constructed of various thicknesses of neoprene that offer different thermal ratings and buoyancy. The relative thickness of sole makes some boots appropriate for walking on rocks with others only intended for lightweight duty.

Many boots have side zippers, but those without zips are definitely worthy of your consideration. Zippers may break or fall down easily and may not be properly sized to fit women's calves. In general, many women complain that they cannot get standard boot zips done up all the way. For this reason, manufacturers such as Aqualung decided to design a boot without zippers that was properly sized for a woman's calf and made of material that was easy to slip on.

The interior construction of boots is important too. The material should be soft without seams that can rub wet skin raw. They may or may not be offered with arch support that might be important to you.

Men's Versus Women's Styles

Men's feet tend to be wider than women's feet. A woman's specific boot is generally narrower in the foot and wider at the calf.

Jill's Opinions

With the number of hours I spend underwater on a project, I might be wet for four or more hours a day. I find that a pair of slick Lycra socks help me get my boots on easily and protects my tender skin from blistering. Men seem to be able to tolerate rough seams and poor construction better than women. Our soft skin gets fragile when wet. Make sure you won't be sidelined by abrasions and blisters.

Reneé's Opinions

Funny how we are made so different! In the past I haven't liked the slick Lycra socks because my foot is already swimming in the bootie. The socks made it worse so I used a thick running sock or a SmartWool sock under the boot. Zippers on my booties are always a fail. Being short, my calf flairs close to the ankle bone. If the zipper is capable of zipping all the way to the top, then the boots are too big. I love my Aqualung Ellie Ergo boots! Finally a boot that fits. Admittedly, I have started using the Lycra socks with these boots and I find this combination works for me.

Exposure Protection— Gloves

Gloves have many varied roles in diving. They be used for abrasion protection when diving on warm water wrecks or catching lobster and as essential thermal protection for women diving in cold water or under the ice. They need to be very well made and fit properly to allow you to perform at your very best. Dexterity is essential when you need to unclip a light or re-fasten a weight belt.

Ensure that the fingers of your gloves are long enough that they fully cover each finger for full mobility and nest down into the web between each digit. Excess finger length in a glove will also lessen dexterity. Photo: Jill Heinerth

Heated undergloves are the newest rage for cold water divers. They are worn underneath dry gloves which attach to the suit with a compression ring system or pull over top of a sealing band on the suit. Photo: Jill Heinerth

General Features

From lightweight wet gloves to heavy neoprene three-finger mitts and fully integrated dry gloves, hand protection comes with many assorted features. Santi recently added heated gloves to their drysuit line while other companies focused on larger areas of the market with advances to their warm water glove line. Aqualung offers women's specific models in two weights. They are designed with longer and narrower palms and shaped fingers that anatomically fit the female hand. Other features to look at include high stretch materials for comfort, heavy coatings and fabrics for heavy duty work, rubberized palms for grip, thinner neoprene palms for better dexterity and heavy backings for warmth.

The wiring for heated gloves runs inside the diver's undergarment (top) and under the wrist seal and is snapped to the underglove connection. Your diving partner can assist with donning the dry glove itself and checking it for security (bottom). Photos: Courtesy of www.SednaEpic.com - Jill Heinerth.

Fit/Sizing

Men's hands tend to be significantly wider in the palm and their fingers are fatter. When women try to wear men's gloves they may find the fingers are too short, especially if they have long nails. Some women have the opposite problem, when their fingers are far shorter than the fingers in the gloves. Both issues create mobility and dexterity issues. It is already hard enough to operate some clips. Add a 7 mm glove that doesn't fit and cold fingers and you have a recipe for disaster. Gloves may seem like an unimportant piece of equipment at first sight, but they are key to dexterity and comfort.

Materials

Fabric, Kevlar, neoprene, rubber and latex are all used to create varying degrees of protection and warmth. Dry gloves pair with warm under-gloves made from materials ranging from Merino wool to Thinsulate, Capilene, polypropylene and nylon.

Special Considerations

When you try on a pair of gloves push the fingers all the way down as far as they will go to ensure the fingers fit and permit you to operate clips and buckles. Consider the length of the gauntlet and how it will overlap the wrists on your suit. You don't want to leave any gaps. Also consider how you will wear your computers and other wrist accessories. You may need a strap extension for your computer.

Jill's Opinions

When I am wearing wet gloves, one of the warmest options I have found is to wear thin 1 mm surfing gloves as the first layer. These gloves have a rather sticky rubber on the outside. I turn them inside out so the sticky side is sealed snugly against my skin. They keep my hands warm while I am getting dressed on the ice or on a boat. Once I am fully dressed and have completed all pre-dive checks, I then put heavy 7 mm wet lobster mitts with a long gauntlet on last. The interior gloves keep my hands almost dry and prevent water from sloshing around. The over gloves add the thermal protection I need. Of course, ever since my new Santi heated dry gloves arrived for Christmas, it is a whole new chapter in comfort and a huge improvement over my former dry glove system. I can now keep my hands truly warm and comfortable.

Reneé's Opinions

I rarely wear gloves diving in the relatively warmer waters of the Florida springs and offshore reefs. Gloves, like boots, have always been a challenge for me. In recent years a few manufacturers have designed smaller reef and neoprene gloves that fit. Aqualung has done an exceptional job on their glove options for women.

Women Mentors

Evelyn Dudas - Pioneering Technical Diver & Custom Suit Manufacturer

Evelyn Bartram Dudas is considered by many to be the the the most famous female wreck diver in history. Since 1965 Evelyn has been diving the North Atlantic wrecks. She was the first woman to dive the Andrea Doria in 1967, while accompanying John Dudas, who recovered the main compass and brass binnacle cover from the then-intact wheel house. She was very frustrated by the lack of proper SCUBA equipment for women. In 1965 she

decided to design, assemble, and sell women's wetsuits in the incongruous setting of an old barn on her family's ancestral property in Westtown, Pennsylvania. After the untimely death of her husband in 1982, as a result of a diving accident, she continued to expand Dudas Diving Duds into a full service dive shop while raising four children as a single

parent. Her full service recreational and technical dive shop is still active near West Chester, Pennsylvania.

Evelyn returned to the Doria again in 1992 and sought further training in Trimix with Billy Deans and Full Cave with Tom Mount. Evie is hobbled by osteoporosis that she thinks is due to improper decompression in her early diving years. She is a fighter and a survivor, not allowing physical challenges to get in the way of her diving pursuits. She has become an avid cave diver and teaches DPV classes both in open water and overhead environments. Photography is still a passionate hobby of hers. Worldwide travels to wrecks in Truk, Bikini, Vanuatu, Grenada, North Carolina, the St. Lawrence River and Tobermory occupy much of the traveling she does now. As an active open water NAUI instructor Evie teaches kids camps in the summer.

Evie is an inaugural inductee into the Women Divers Hall of Fame, a member of the Philadelphia Chapter of the Explorers Club and program manager of Keystone Divers Association. Evie is a diving legend and mentor to many and is still very active in diving well into her sixties.

Exposure Protection— After-Dive Wear

Whether you live in the Caribbean or the northern Europe, you can get chilled in any temperature. Bringing along the right after-dive clothing makes all the difference. If you are planning on a second dive, staying warm in-between dives is critical to your comfort and safety.

General Features

Long dive parkas, rain and wind protection, warm hats and gloves are all essential gear on a boat. Wind chill at any temperature will rob your warmth quickly. Get out of your suit after diving and get into something warm and dry. Dive parkas and ponchos can give you a little changing privacy when there is no place to hide on an open boat or help reduce wind chill if you are getting back in the water after a short interval.

This unique clothing from Dive Sangha features built in buttons for hanging your clothes on the line. Dry clothing is essential for getting warm. Photo: Jill Heinerth

Jill's Opinions

I'm sort of a climate refugee. I left Canada and moved to the Caribbean and then on to Florida. Still, I have often come home with a significantly lowered core temperature after a day of diving. My friends tease me when I wear a winter hat in Florida, but keeping my head warm is really import for my overall comfort.

Reneé's Opinions

I'm of the mindset that being warm is more favorable than looking cool. Since living in Florida, I've joked that we often look like homeless people wearing mismatched bits and pieces of thermal protection that may not be stylish but still get the job done. I always have rain gear on hand to throw on over a wetsuit or dry clothes. Rain gear will not only keep me dry, it blocks wind which is critical to thermal protection. I'm with Jill on the hat. I can often be seen wearing my toque even in Florida. However instead of "CANADA" it says "Fourth Element" or "Santi!"

Exposure Protection— Artificial Heating

With battery technology shrinking, many manufacturers are jumping into the arena of artificial heat. What was once powered by a fifteen pound battery can how be donned with little additional weight. The options are expanding rapidly.

General Features

Wetsuit heaters by Thermolution and other manufacturers come in the form of a heavy Lycra or Thinsulate style shirt with special low profile battery pockets and internally disguised wiring. The heat is emitted from the network of wires contained in the shirt.

Drysuit heaters may be constructed in a similar fashion as wetsuit heaters or be integrated into custom fitted full length undergarments or long vests. The batteries may be

Thermolution manufactures heated undergarments that can be worn when wet. They are operated with a wireless remote or wired controller and are available at HeatedWetsuits.com. Photo: Jill Heinerth

contained in the garment as in the case of Thermolution and operated with a wireless transmitter or may be powered by external battery packs that are plugged into a port that is integrated in the dry suit inflator mechanism. In this case, the diver can choose the size of the battery pack to fit the length of the dive(s).

Special Considerations

There are not too many suppliers of heated garments at this point, but it is a rapidly growing facet of diving. Research your choices carefully to ensure they are manufactured reliably and will not break the first time you jump in the water or pull a garment over your head. Social media may offer helpful reviews of specific products.

Artificially heating parts of your body during different phases of your dive may cause physiological effects that have not been considered in the decompression algorithm of your diving computer. If you are relatively uniformly warm during your entire dive, it is not an issue. However, if you go from very cold to a high heat setting on your garment or the reverse, this may affect your on gassing and off gassing differently than anticipated. Studies are being conducted at DAN and we focus on these issues in the physiological section of the book.

Men's Versus Women's Styles

Many shirt and vest options are completely unisex, so expect the sizes to be a little large and the styling boxy.

Jill's Opinions

I tried my first dry suit heater on an expedition in Antarctica and was pleasantly surprised with the added comfort. Unfortunately, the battery technology of the time was very bulky and heavy. These days many more options are available. Today, my Santi heating system keeps me toasty with a variety of pieces to fit different applications.

I enjoy having a bit of extra warmth on wetsuit dives too and use a simple shirt from HeatedWetsuits.com.

A full heating package includes a suit or vest, heated gloves, replacement dual purpose valve for the drysuit and external battery pack sized for desired duration. Photo: Courtesy: Santi Diving

Reneé's Opinions

I use the Thermolution heated Lycra shirt when I'm teaching in a wetsuit for extended hours in a day. It fits great and I don't even notice the batteries. The battery life isn't great so I budget when I have it switched on. These are currently quite expensive, but are far less expensive than a drysuit.

Regulators

It may seem that there are few things you can do with a breathing apparatus that would make it more desirable for women, but some manufacturers have found an edge for the female market. Styling and weight appear to be important to women.

General Features

Some manufacturers have downsized the second stage on their regulator while still maintaining high performance breathing characteristics. Mouthpieces are often offered in regular and small sizes to please women of all sizes and reduce jaw fatigue. In some cases, an optional, removable lip shield keeps your face even warmer than standard mouthpieces.

Jill's Opinions

Choose your regulator based on the right performance specifications for the type of diving that you do. You can always add a smaller mouthpiece or a Seacure moldable mouthpiece for added comfort and reduced jaw fatigue. I always use Seacure mouthpieces. Trimmed and molded correctly, they are extremely comfortable and last for many years. I still have some that have been in service for over ten years.

Reneé's Opinions

I've not found the weight of second stages to be an issue for me. I love that there are smaller, more comfortable mouthpieces available now. A few months ago I reluctantly (kicking and screaming) tried a Seacure mouthpiece. I just bought my second one for another regulator and will continue to replace chewed up mouthpieces with Seacure. They are available in colors that are more attractive than the original clear. What an unexpected surprise with amazing value!

Navigation Aids/Compasses

There are really no specific navigation aids designed for women, but we have to find a place to put these devices on our bodies. Women with short arms have very little space available for multiple devices attached to their wrists. Furthermore, the devices are so wide, that even when the strap is cinched, it wants to spin around your arm freely. Suunto

recently addressed the issue of wrist size by designing a product that specifically fits smaller wrists well. Hopefully they will carry that through their entire product line. Some women have resorted to putting some of the wrist-mounted gear into their suit pocket or accessory pocket, bringing it out only when needed. Another solution is to remove the standard wide band on a wrist device and replace it with stretchy bungee material. The device will slide over the hand and snug in place without moving. There is also no need to fuss with challenging buckles when you are wearing gloves. Retractors and clips can also help you put things away securely.

A compass on a retractor may work better than piling more gear on short arms (above). It is really important to keep accessory gear streamlined, especially to avoid snags and damage to the environment (below). Photos: Jill Heinerth

Accessory Gear

When it comes to a woman's dive gear, accessories are many times the icing on the cake. Once gear has been selected, the fun begins and it is time to put it all together. Functional gadgetry is available in every dive shop and all over the Internet and includes items such as lights, slates, safety sausages, pocket masks, cameras, knives, pocket snorkels and weights. A problem for many women is where to put these items. Many of today's BCDs and harnesses are loaded with a plethora of accessory attachment points such as D-rings, clips, snaps and Velcro from which to hang something. If not careful, a diver will soon resemble something like a Christmas tree covered with ornaments! Put that diver in a horizontal position and suddenly everything hangs downward creating the human wind chime. Put this diver over a reef, in a shipwreck or a cave and the situation becomes dangerous. So how does a woman diver take the things we need and keep critical equipment, such as our alternate air source, safely available? A good place to start is to simply bring only what you need for the dive. Recognize that every single item that is on our bodies while diving creates a sort of exoskeleton, resulting in increased resistance. Make a gear list of items that you feel are essential and begin thinking of where to store them. A D-ring may seem like the obvious choice, but may not be the best choice.

Accessory Gear— Lights

One would think that lights have few specific issues for women, but there are a number of simple considerations and tips for choosing the right lights and associated accessories. Lights are becoming increasingly more compact making them easier to store and access.

Before you buy any light, think about how and where you will stow it. Dangling accessories are a bad idea at any level of diving, and especially important to avoid on live reef environments. If you plan to carry your light in a pocket, ensure your BCD or suit pocket will accommodate the light in a way that still allows you to reach that pocket when you want to deploy or stow the light. If the light does not come with a clip, ensure it has a place to put one that will enable it to be installed in a streamlined way on your harness or BCD or clipped into a pocket for added security. The light will need to be secured so it doesn't dangle and cause damage to it or the environment while in a good horizontal diving position. Currently there are a plethora of primary and backup dive lights on the market that come with an attached wrist lanyard. If you choose to use a lanyard, be sure the opening is long enough to go around your wrist and short enough so it isn't excessively dangly. Your mask is also a great place to secure a small backup light. Be considerate of others if you need to have this light on while night diving!

Soft hand mounts are a great solution for carrying lights. Light & Motion makes a small sized hand mount for their Sola and Gobe lights that are well sized for petite women. Photo: Jill Heinerth

Remove the light and use it hand-held so your buddy won't be blinded. If your BCD or harness has a shoulder D-ring, consider clipping the light there.

If you are purchasing a canister light, follow the same line of thought. Think about where you will secure it first; on the waist strap, on the butt plate of a sidemount rig or perhaps clipped to the BCD in some way. With a canister light, you want to check to see that the cord is long enough for your reach. You might need a slightly longer cord for butt-mounting your light on a sidemount rig. The manufacturer may provide that at no additional charge at the point of order, but may have to charge a fee for a later retrofit. If you have short arms, you may wonder about what to do with all that extra cord length. Some manufacturers will cut a shorter custom cord for you. It is certainly better than dragging an extra loop over the bottom, though you can also wrap additional length around your arm.

Jill's Opinions

Canister lights often come with Goodman handles that hand-mount the light head on a device that gives the diver full dexterity without dropping the light. These handles, often made of metal or Delrin, are usually much wider than a woman's hand. They are adjustable, but are still very bulky and often too large for most women's hands. Without gloves, I have never been able to get even close to a reasonable fit and they usually cut

Halcyon's solution to the Goodman handle is to offer both vertical and horizontal quick adjustment to fit a maximum number of hands with or without gloves. Photo: Jill Heinerth

the skin on the back of my hand in any case. Soft Goodman handles made with an elastic or fabric strap fit a much wider range of women. Several manufacturers also make very comfortable glove-like soft hand mounts that fit a wide range of hands and lights. I still find myself in the small size of most of these products since they are usually sized for men wearing big gloves.

Reneé's Opinions

I have the same issue with the traditional Goodman handle. My hands are small I have a hard time holding my light head while pulling myself into high flow caves. Recently DiveRite customized their quick releasing soft hand mount just for me! Like many people I prefer small lights that pack a punch. The Sola and Gone lights by Light & Motion are quite remarkable! I love my Light Monkey hand held backup lights too.

In the open water only, I wear my Suunto compass on a small retractor that is out of the way when I don't need it and accessible when I do.

Careers in Diving

Sylvia Ledbetter - Manufacturer's Sales Rep and Consultant

Sylvia Ledbetter and her husband Bob are independent sales representatives who have become enduring success stories in the dive industry. Their experience and mentoring has helped shops through the southeast and Caribbean become more effective retailers.

After earning a degree in nursing from the University of Tennessee, Sylvia married Bob and soon moved to Gainesville, Florida to represent numerous brands of dive gear. Today, they work tirelessly visiting shops across Florida representing Sherwood, Genesis, Akona and Ikelite. As small business owners, they have found a way to survive in difficult economic times while nurturing a long and happy marriage. They believe that their personal touch helps support the local "brick and mortar" retailer who is best able to provide quality service and seasoned instruction that ensures the industry's success.

Photos: Jill Heinerth and Bob Ledbetter

Accessory Gear- Knives

Knives are a practical tool for cutting or prying. Many BCDs have grommets installed that accommodate a specific knife. Your knife doesn't need to be huge to be effective. A small 3-4 inch blade will do the trick for most situations. Some recreational divers choose to carry a Z-knife on their chest strap, shoulder strap or watch/computer band. These are small, lightweight and don't take up a lot of room. The Z-knife is a great tool for cutting fishing line, for example, in case of entanglement. Z-knives originally came from the skydiving community for emergency line cuts and are now also purpose built for diving.

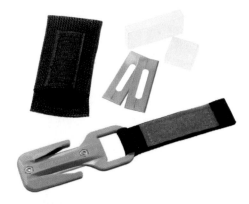

The Eezycut Trilobite knife is a simple, streamlined device with a razor sharp edge and replaceable blades..

Jill's Opinions

I'm a big fan of the Trilobite knives. They are razor sharp without any way for me to cut myself. I always wear one that is easily accessible on a computer wrist strap and I also wear a backup cutter on a waist or chest strap. They come with additional blades that can be quickly swapped when one gets dull. Other Z-knife designs are disposable when the blade deteriorates.

Reneé's Opinions

I love the Z-knife style. I got teased for wearing one on an open water dive mere minutes before I cut loose from some fishing line! On a dive in Utila I spotted a small piece of fire coral draped in a plastic bag from the grocery store. Holding the grip of the Z-knife while taking advantage of the curved blade, my buddy and I were able to gently remove the bag without harming the coral or humans. These compact knives can be easily stored on the BCD itself, in a pocket or even on a watch or computer band. Small blunt tipped knives are great for prying and I like that some BCDs have a built in spot for them. Dive Rite makes their line cutter with Velcro that will fit over any strap without the need to unthread anything.

If your arm is already loaded with gear, try using an underwater notebook that can be secured in a pocket.

Accessory Gear- Slates/Writing

Women with short arms who want to wear two computers and wrist slates on an arm just can't find the space. As you age, and your eyes deteriorate, it is even less possible. You can fill your arm with slates and computers all you want, but you won't be able to read them as they march up your arm. For quick writing access try using a small multipage wrist slate with a pencil. A ponytail holder can secure the pencil to the slates. If you don't have wrist space, multi page slates can be secured with a double ended clip to a D-ring or just about anywhere that doesn't cause damage to the environment or impede access to gas supply or inflators. If you simply don't have the space, consider using a notebook and pencil that can be stowed in a pocket.

Accessory Gear—Dive Bags

A sturdy bag with wheels will help you get gear to the boat or dive site easily. Photo: Courtesy of AquaLung

Gear bags are not so much women specific as they are size specific. Any shorter person will tell you that it is tough to pick up an aluminum 80 cft /12 liter tank by the valve because they have to bend their elbow to get it up off the ground or are forced to carry it horizontally. Gear bags can have the same issue. Some are so tall that they are a challenge to walk with or carry up the stairs. We all want to carry as much as possible in one bag but have to be realistic about our carrying capacity. Roller dive bags and duffles can be very handy, but they may not travel over the terrain at your dive site or resort. Standard duffles have a huge capacity, but may be too heavy to handle or ship on a passenger aircraft. These days we have to carefully divide up equipment and clothing in a couple of bags to meet weight requirements.

Safety Devices— Apps

A clever app can give your family peace of mind when you are diving. "Be Back Soon" can be installed on your iPhone and has great functionality for dives and other purposes. It was originally intended for people to file a dive plan before heading out on a trip. The user inputs an expected time for return. At fifteen minutes prior to that time, a ring tone and message are sent to the diver reminding them to turn off the alert. Five minutes prior to deadline, the alarm and message are repeated. If the diver is overdue, a message is sent to selected people to let them know. You control the message by inputting something simple like, "I'm on the vessel Seascaper out of Puerto Avontigua and we are expected back at 4pm. Please check with the Coast Guard if you have not heard from me before 5pm." You can also make a more urgent message such as, "I'm cave diving at Ginnie Springs. If I do not answer my cell phone now, please call 911. I am overdue." It offers a terrific service for remote or solo divers and excellent accountability for any diver.

We've added mention of this app here because it may be of more interest to women than men. It is nice to know that someone will come looking for you if you are overdue. Of course, it also has great value out of the water when you head out for a first date or even to track your kids who are out for the evening and have a curfew. For diving and beyond, it is a reliable watchdog.

Women Mentors

Cristina Zenato - Dive Trainer and Shark Handler

Cristina Zenato's career qualifies her to be in the category of world's most dangerous jobs. If handling wild sharks is not enough, she is also a recognized cave diving explorer and instructor. Yet although she operates in a decidedly male world, she places a high value on authenticity, tenacity and celebration of her femininity.

Cristina moved from Italy to the Bahamas in 1994 and decided to make it her home and diving her life. She manages a team of eighteen divers, teaches hundreds of students at all levels from Open Water to Full Cave and specializes in teaching a program on shark handling. While weighted down in a heavily armored chainmail suit, she gracefully coaxes a shark into a status of tonic immobility through

gentle touch. She explores and maps cave systems, providing the Bahamian government with vital information for natural resource protection and is the first woman to have connected a land cave with an ocean blue hole. She consults with organizations for the creation of marine parks with an emphasis on protecting sharks. Cristina believes there is great power in education and volunteers her time to host foreign students and teach local Bahamian school children to dive as part of sharing her vision.

One of the greatest challenges Cristina faces as a woman diver seeking equality is learning how to demonstrate strength and resilience without sacrificing her femininity. Uniquely connecting well with both women and men students has been rewarding to Cristina.

Cristina has spent years fighting with dive gear that did not fit. Instead of it working for her, she felt overpowered by it. She had to find unique solutions especially with her drysuit and sidemount harness. In the most recent years those issues have been resolved and now she has gear to suit her body size.

She recalls an awkward moment years ago when she was in a grocery store with a visibly older cave diving colleague. He was buying adult diapers and lubricating jelly for his drysuit seals. "The facial expression of the cashier was priceless!"

With the increase of women in our sport it is evident that we need equipment that both fits and performs. Fortunately, the attitude that women are inferior and weak seems to be declining. Cristina Zenato believes that women can be strong and feminine at the same time. This new perception is exemplified by her lifestyle, career and passion for the environment that screams, "Be who you are!"

Storage Solutions

A nice bellows pocket or two on your wetsuit or drysuit, neoprene shorts with pockets or a clip-on thigh pocket provide storage for extra lights, slates, a small repair kit, pocket snorkel, pocket mask, etc. Pockets can be glued on as after market additions or worn as attachments that come with clips and webbing that fasten to your harness or BCD waist. Consider wearing a thick neoprene hood with a thin Lycra hood on top. Very small items such as defog, a pencil or a small light can be stuffed underneath the outer hood securely. Another creative location for storage is on the tank itself. Add a large D-ring to the tank cam band. A bolt snap, can be affixed to nearly any accessory item that can then be clipped to the D-ring. This is an accessible spot for items that may not be frequently needed such as a small repair kit with O-rings and tools, a safety sausage, or lift bag with reel. There are countless storage possibilities so get creative about staying safe and streamlined.

Light Monkey makes a pocket that can be glued onto wet or drysuits, offering plenty of storage space for accessory gear. Photo: Courtesy of Light Monkey

Jill's Opinions

I'm a big fan of thigh pockets for storage. I feel more secure knowing things are properly clipped inside a pocket instead of hanging off my body. I install bungee loops inside the pocket so that each item is safely clipped in case the pocket falls open. If I have to carry a lot of additional gear such as sampling bottles or survey gear, I use an accessory pocket that can be secured behind me with a clip. My dear friend and colleague Brian Kakuk calls this his "man bag" or his "murse."

Reneé's Opinions

I am five feet tall and finding room to stow things is always a challenge for me. BCD pockets are great, but I find them difficult to reach into on a small BCD that actually fits me. I really like bellows pockets on the thigh region of my exposure suits. Inside each pocket is a place to clip lights, my car key, etc., so they can't float away or be lost. Because I don't have much available space it is especially critical that I don't clutter up my upper body. I've got room for regulators and that's about it, so nothing else goes there. I also will take advantage of a D-ring on a single tank to clip my small repair kit or lift bag and reel if needed. I've had to modify harnesses from the factory because I couldn't reach things or make adjustments. Again, just because it says "small" doesn't mean it fits! I like to think I invented the secret storage between two hoods. I use it all the time during research dives! I will never be seen with stuff clipped all over me and dangling. I used to only wear my Z-knife on my watch band, but now I also have one on my harness shoulder strap for easy access. I've learned to do touch drills with every single piece of equipment on me to make sure I can reach it and to ensure it can be easily deployed and replaced without obstructing my regulator or alternate air source.

Technical Gear

Technical diving gear designed specifically for women has been almost non-existent until very recently. It seems that manufacturers look at the population of women divers and only see a niche within a niche of diving. However, it is worth considering which comes first— the chicken or the egg? If more women had working, comfortable technical diving equipment then they might not feel that there are so many barriers to entering this advanced end of the sport. Large women often struggle to find the right fit, but smaller women have been completely overlooked. Women are not just frustrated by fit, but also grapple with training standards and regimens that are only tested on men. Small women also have to strain under the mass of equipment that often outweighs them. There are many hurdles in technical diving that need to be overcome. Hopefully this section will help you jump over a few.

Technical diving instructor Marissa Lasso prepares for a dive in the cave at Ginnie Springs in Florida. Photo: Jill Heinerth

Y-valves/H-valves

For many divers, their first move toward technical diving might be in a single tank cavern diving class. These programs may be conducted with a standard single tank or in a single tank with dual outlet Y- or H-valve. Dual outlet valves permit two separate first stages to be attached to a tank, thus offering redundancy of gas delivery. Each first stage is equipped with a second stage. An inflator and SPG are fitted in addition to a separate LP hose for drysuit divers.

General Features

Y- and H-valves are usually supplied as a 200-bar DIN valve with a removable insert so that divers can use DIN or standard yoke configurations. Some very old valves only offer standard yoke attachments.

Hollis H-valve with removable DIN inserts.
Photo: Courtesy of Hollis

Fit/Sizing

The problem with Y- or H- valves on single tanks is that they are utilized in diving that requires quite a lot of additional accessory gear and perhaps larger tanks. They are often used with recreational BCDs that do not support larger tanks well. The additional accessory gear used in cavern or other technical diving becomes a bit of a nightmare to streamline. Small women may find there is simply "too much stuff" to carry without enough useful attachment points for the extra gear. If you are considering diving in the overhead environment you may have an easier time with an appropriate set of small double tanks.

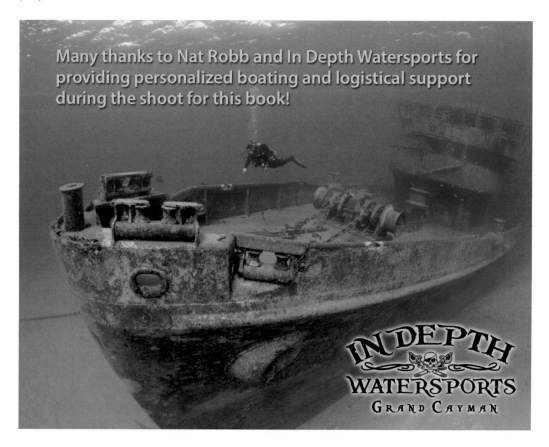

Many thanks to Nat Robb and In Depth Watersports for providing personalized boating and logistical support during the shoot for this book!

Jill's Opinions

I stopped teaching people cavern classes in single tanks with Y- and H-valves and decided I only wanted to work with people diving in double tank configurations. It is possible to safely dive in a cavern with a single tank, but I find the gear streamlining and management to be much more effective in a lightweight set of doubles or small sidemounted tanks. The buoyancy control is definitely easier. Imagine a single tank to be like a boat that is too top-heavy. It wants to roll over. A good set of small doubles has better weight distribution across your back allowing you to hang off the doubles rather than fight the high center of gravity.

PADI Course Director Pam Wooten and her diving partner, Cave Diving Instructor Van Fleming, using back mounted doubles for cave diving. This is still likely the most popular technical diving configuration. Photo: Jill Heinerth

The one instance where I find an H-valve to be useful is in the case of "no-mounting" a single tank in an extreme form of cave diving. In this case, the single tank is pushed ahead of the diver in order to pass through tiny spaces. The redundancy of regulators is critical to ensuring safety in case you get hung up.

Reneé's Opinions

Even though I'm small, I haven't had too much trouble with sizing regarding my tec diving harnesses. I've stuck with DiveRite, who will completely customize a harness specifically for me. They make me feel like I'm part of the diving community instead of being overlooked and handed something "small" and expected to "deal with it."

I am very accustomed to teaching cavern courses with students in a single tank and recreational BCD. We spend quite a bit of time reconfiguring and streamlining. If someone wants to progress beyond Cavern to the Full Cave level, then that's a different story and I want to move them into a double configuration right away and bypass the single tank configuration completely.

Double Tanks

The first time you saw a set of double tanks in a dive shop you might have tried to pick them up. Shocked at the weight, that might have been the end of your dreams of technical diving. Many North American divers purchase enormous twin tank sets thinking the increased volume will buy them more time underwater. Normally these huge, negatively buoyant tanks only cost them increased air consumption, gas lost to buoyancy control, and a hernia at the fill station. If you travel to other parts of the world, you will find that both genders of divers have recognized that smaller sets of steel double tanks are more efficient to swim and carry. Almost any size of tank can be banded together as doubles for redundancy. If extra gas is needed, it can always be staged with aluminum cylinders.

General Features

Double backmounted tanks are connected with stainless steel bands and a manifold. Independent backmounted doubles with separate independent valves are almost unheard of these days. The bands on the tanks are generally spaced so that a standard backplate with holes that are 11-inches apart may be affixed to protruding bolts with wing nuts.

If you choose to boat dive with double tanks, find out about the entry and exit procedures before you book the charter. Some boats have ladders while others are equipped with modern lifts. This may affect who you decide to dive with. Photo: Jill Heinerth

Fit/Sizing

Tanks of any size can be turned into doubles. Women generally have better breathing gas consumption than their male counterparts and may be able to use smaller gas cylinders for diving. Though many men frown on small tanks, they may be all you need for the type of diving you are seeking. There is nothing wrong with banding together a set of double 45 cft tanks. You'll have the redundancy of dual valves and the comfort of a rig that only weighs a little more than a single tank setup.

Dive cylinders are designed for horizontal underwater use so the increased vertical burden and weight on land is much higher. The water to air transition is rarely fun. Gear up prepared to manage the walk to and from the water (or use a hand truck instead). No matter if it's a boat ladder, a surf entry or an unstable slope into a spring, the physics are the same. Double tanks weigh a lot. Fortunately, tank manufacturers have begun to design shorter high volume cylinders that are perfect for a shorter diver, making the walk to the site easier.

One thing to consider when using small tanks is that the volume of those tanks will affect the turnaround time of your dive. If your male partner is wearing double 104 cft tanks and you are only wearing double 45 cft tanks, then there is a serious mismatch. You always need to reserve enough gas to get you and your buddy back to the surface safely. You might not breathe much when using those tiny tanks but your partner will be breathing significantly more. There may come a day when he needs gas from you, so ensure you have fully thought through the types of diving and buddies you want to be involved with before choosing your tank size.

Whether you are diving in a single cylinder or double cylinder configuration find the equipment that works best for your application. Try before you buy when possible and ask experienced divers or dive professionals for advice when choosing the right cylinders.

Materials

To date, the only reasonably priced tank materials are steel and aluminum. In general aluminum tanks are more positively buoyant than steel, but there is a big difference between models and manufacturers. The charts on the following pages will help you select a tank based on your own personal buoyancy and your ability to lift a set of doubles into the back of your vehicle. Note the difference in weight between full and empty cylinders. The swing in buoyancy can be significant and you will have to plan for that in your personal weighting and wing's lift capacity.

These partly used aluminum stage bottles demonstrate how the bottoms of these tanks tend to float upwards as they empty. Photo: Jill Heinerth

Common Tanks

The following charts list many commonly available cylinders and their weight and size specifications. If your tank is not listed here, ask the manufacturer for similar specifications to help you predict buoyancy changes if you switch to another brand or model of tank. Imperial measurements are shown in the top half of the chart in yellow. Metric measurements are shown in the bottom half of the chart in blue. All buoyancy figures have been calculated in sea water with a valve present but not a regulator.

A pile of tanks awaits the dive team preparing to enter Dan's Cave in Abaco. Photo: Jill Heinerth

LUXFER ALUMINUM	AL40	AL50	AL63	AL80	ALN80*
Service Pressure (psi)	3000	3000	3000	3000	3300
True Capacity	40 cft	48.4 cft	63 cft	77.4 cft	77.4 cft
Buoyancy Full (lbs)	-2.3	-2.2	-1.4	-5.7	-4.3
Buoyancy 500 psi (lbs)	+1.4	+0.8	+1.7	+3.4	-0.9
Weight Empty	21.2	26.7	31.4	35.4	41
Outer Diameter (inches)	6.9	7.25	7.25	7.25	8
Length (inches)	19	21.9	26.1	25.8	26.2
Service pressure (bar)	207	207	207	207	228
Internal Volume (liters)	5.7	6.9	9	11.1	10.3
Buoyancy Full (kg)	-0.3	-1	-0.6	-2.6	-2
Buoyancy Empty (kg)	+1	+.6	+1.2	+.2	+.02
Weight Empty	6.9	9.6	12.1	14.2	16.1
Outer Diameter (mm)	133	175	184	184	184
Length (cm)	62.9	48.3	55.5	66.2	65.6

* The ALN80 version of Luxfer tank is also frequently referred to as a "Neutral 80."

To read our ongoing blog visit:
WomenUnderwater.com

XS SCUBA	X7-65	X7-80	X7-100	X7-120	X8-119
Material	steel	steel	steel	steel	steel
Service Pressure (psi)	3442	3442	3442	3442	3442
True Capacity @ 2640 psi	66.4 cft	81 cft	99.5 cft	120.6 cft	123 cft
Buoyancy Full (lbs)	-8.7	-9	-10	-11	-10.9
Buoyancy Empty (lbs)	-3.9	-3	-2.5	-2	-2
Weight Empty	25.1	29.9	33.1	39.7	42.5
Outer Diameter (inches)	7.25	7.25	7.25	7.25	8
Length (inches)	16.7	19.8	22.7	27.7	23.9
Service pressure (bar)	230	230	230	230	230
Internal Volume (liters)	8.2	10.1	12.2	15.3	14.8
Buoyancy Full (kg)	-3.9	-4.1	-4.5	-4.9	-4.9
Buoyancy Empty (kg)	-1.8	-1.4	-1.1	-0.9	-0.9
Weight Empty	11.4	13.1	15	17.2	19
Outer Diameter (mm)	184	184	184	184	203
Length (cm)	42.2	50	60.1	71.1	60.1

BLUE STEEL FABER	L27DV	L50DVB	L85DVB	M71DVB	M100DVB
Material	steel	steel	steel	steel	steel
Service Pressure (psi)	2640	2640	2640	3300	3498
True Capacity	27 cft	50 cft	85 cft	71 cft	100 cft
Buoyancy Full (lbs)	-3	-2.4	-3.8	-4.4	-14.1
Buoyancy Empty (lbs)	-1.1	-1.2	-2.3	-0.9	-6.7
Weight Empty	11.7	18.9	31.2	28.7	38.7
Outer Diameter (inches)	5.5	5.5	7	6.8	7.25
Length (inches)	14.4	25.2	26	20.5	24.2
Service pressure (bar)	180	180	180	225	240
Internal Volume (liters)	4	8	13	9	12

WORTHINGTON	LP27	LP77	LP85	LP95	LP108
Material	steel	steel	steel	steel	steel
Service Pressure (psi)	2400+	2400+	2400+	2400+	2400+
True Capacity @ 2640 psi	27 cft	77 cft	82.9 cft	93.3 cft	108.6
Buoyancy Full (lbs)	-3	-6.8	-7.1	-10.1	-10.7
Buoyancy Empty (lbs)	-1	-1	-0.7	-3	-2.6
Weight Empty	11.9	32.5	36.8	41.9	45.9
Outer Diameter (inches)	14.5	23.2	24.7	23.7	26.5
Length (inches)	14.5	23.2	24.7	23.7	26.5
Service pressure (bar)	166+	166+	166+	166+	166+
Water Capacity (liters)	4.3	12	12.8	14.8	16.8
Buoyancy Full (kg)	-1.4	-2.7	-2.7	-3.6	-3.6
Buoyancy Empty (kg)	-0.5	-1	-1	-1.5	-0.5
Weight Empty	5.4	15.6	16.7	18.5	20.2
Outer Diameter (mm)	140	184	184	203	203
Length (cm)	36.8	65.3	65.3	60.1	67.9

Jill's Opinions

I have always preferred to wear my weight as usable gas. When it comes to maximizing a set of doubles, my favorites are a pair of steel LP85s. They have a reasonable volume, are not too tall to pick up on land and are manageable without assistance. They are about the size of a pair of aluminum 80 cft tanks but carry significantly more volume and negative buoyancy. They weigh virtually the same on land. I'd rather use the steel tanks and avoid needing lead weight than carry less volume and be forced to carry lead.

Technical dive shops routinely over fill steel LP tanks beyond rated pressure and that means my doubles will have significantly more gas than the aluminum tanks.

Reneé's Opinions

I used to dive low pressure steel 95s. A few years and an anterior cruciate ligament (ACL) replacement later, I've had to downsize to something I can manage on land easily. Lately when teaching cavern classes I'm using dual low pressure Blue Steel backmount 50s. They are perfect except they are too light to sink my old neoprene drysuit. I have to dive in a 7 mm wetsuit which isn't too bad. When I dive sidemount, I love my OMS 85s. They get a little buoyant as they get lower in gas volume, so I will utilize drop weights so I can safely perform my decompression or safety stops.

Double Tank Harnesses

Harnesses are fastened to a backplate which is fixed to the set of bolts on your doubles with quickly removable thumb screws, wing nuts or wheels. Two holes in the spine region of the plate are spaced 11 inches apart to provide a connection point for the bolts. The buoyancy wing is trapped between the harness/plate system and the tanks.

General Features

The harness itself may be constructed of a single piece of nylon webbing or it may be more complicated with swivels and quick releases, padding and straps. The waist is generally secured with a sliding quick release buckle and a crotch strap is affixed for stability.

The actual plate itself comes in different heights and widths depending on the manufacturer. The slots and holes on a backplate also differ from company to company.

Fit/Sizing

All harnesses are adjustable, but the plate needs to fit to provide the perfect size. If the plate is too long, it will cut into your body and the waistband will be too low on your hips. If the plate is too wide, then the shoulder straps will fall off your shoulders. Several manufacturers offer short plates that are better suited for women's short torsos. If this shorter plate is too narrow for you, some manufacturers have even created short plates with a standard width. One manufacturer has an option of a soft plate style that is great for travel or any time you want to cut down on weight. You may have to try a couple to find one that is right for you.

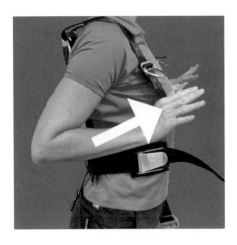

Halcyon's unique cinch harness offers the security of single continuous webbing with full adjustability and an easy release mechanism. The Halcyon harness releases by pulling on the shoulder straps at the correct angle (above). The Halcyon harness slides to tighten by pulling on the waist band at the correct angle (below). Photos: Courtesy of Halcyon

All harnesses fit differently. Even a single piece of webbing can be woven onto the plate in a couple of different of ways either making the shoulders wide or narrow. Some women will find that a chest strap is absolutely necessary to keep the shoulders positioned properly and others may prefer to go without. If you use a chest strap, ensure it does not dig into your breasts or block your drysuit valve.

Padded harnesses increase comfort.
Photo: Courtesy of Halcyon

Materials

Harnesses for double tanks are generally mounted to a solid backplate made of ABS plastic, aluminum, Kydex or stainless steel. There are a few soft harnesses that come with smaller stainless steel stabilizing plates.

Special Considerations

There are numerous features that make a harness easier to get in and out of. Cinch straps at the waist that can be enlarged and shrunk down are helpful. Delrin quick release buckles make harness removal simple and easy. Though some sales people will insist that this is a failure point, you will find that swimming around with one quick release open is very easy. Failure of a buckle is almost a non-issue, whereas comfortably getting in and out of gear is an issue and could be critical in an emergency situation.

Padding on the shoulders adds comfort for those wearing lighter suits. Crotch straps can be made of narrow half-inch or wider two-inch webbing. A crotch strap is absolutely necessary to keep tanks from shifting, especially in a head-down orientation, so find out which one works for you. Your crotch strap becomes a towing harness when you drive a DPV. For long range driving, a V-shaped crotch strap or towing harness may be better. Rather than clipping in to the scooter ring on the crotch strap, try wearing a webbed climbing harness that distributes weight around your legs rather than pulling on your girlie parts.

Some manufacturers make backplates in short styles and alternative widths. Petite women should carefully size their plate to ensure it is comfortable with the weight of doubles without cutting into the lower back or hips. Photo: Courtesy of Halcyon

Jill's Opinions

When I am at home, I use a stainless steel backplate with a webbed harness with quick release buckles. With double steel LP 85s or steel HP 100s, I need no additional weight. When I travel, I take a lighter aluminum backplate to reduce my luggage weight. If I am wearing a wetsuit in salt water I might need a bit of lead, but not much. If I am diving in a drysuit, I integrate a weight into the space between the tanks (known as a V-weight) or use a weight belt. All of my harnesses, including sidemount and rebreather are set up identically so the transition between them is seamless. I can always find things in the same place on each unit.

Reneé's Opinions

Up until very recently there has been a "one size will fit all" mindset with harnesses. Like most things, "one size fits all" isn't necessarily realistic. At the time of writing at least one technical equipment manufacturer is considering women in their harness design process. A woman's harness should fit her. When it does, the chest strap, shoulder and waist D-rings, pouch and weight pockets are better located for ease of accessibility. Deploying and replacing regulators and accessories should not be problematic. If you dive an identical harness to your male buddy, it could be sloppy on you. You'll want to feel integrated with your rig so that you can control it. If you can't control your rig, it will be uncomfortable as well as dangerous.

Double Tank Wings

Wings provide your buoyancy, lifting you and your double tanks appropriately while remaining as streamlined as possible.

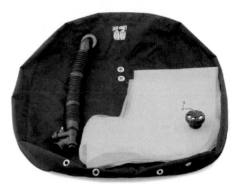

General Features

Wings are made of a variety of fabrics that resist abrasion and can handle repetitive use. Most wings are made of a durable cover with separate interior bladder. Some wings are constructed with dual bladders with completely redundant inflation systems.

Wings for double tanks are generally manufactured with a strong outer cover and durable inflatable bladder. They are specified by their lift capacity. Photo: Courtesy of Light Monkey

Fit/Sizing

Wings come in various lift capacities (volume) and numerous shapes. You will want to match your wing to your required lift and get the buoyancy in the right place. Wings made for rebreathers tend to concentrate lift lower on the hips since rebreather divers are already carrying a volume of air higher on their shoulders in their counterlungs. Some wings are horseshoe-shaped and others let air flow around the wing as in a 360° inflatable donut. Some wings are adjusted by cinching them down with bungee cord and others do not offer that feature. An oversized wing adds unnecessary bulk and width to your profile, forcing you to drag along the extra material. A wing that is properly fitted will supply adequate lift and remain relatively streamlined whether full or empty.

Special Considerations

If you dive in a wetsuit, you should use a redundant wing that supplies backup buoyancy in case you have a failure of the inflation bladder. If you wear a drysuit, you may be able to use your suit as a backup, but you should practice in shallow water. Many small women in heavy tanks would have a difficult to impossible time regaining the surface in the event of a wing failure. You need to be sure you are covered and confident in the event of an emergency.

Backplates should fit the torso of the diver and wings should provide adequate lift without too much excess bulk that can cause drag in the water. Photo: Jill Heinerth

Rebreather harnesses are often similar to tec harnesses and should fit snugly and prevent the rebreather from shifting. Photo: Pam Wooten

Inflator mechanisms and pull dumps should be placed so that you can effectively release expanding gas in both vertical and horizontal positions. Check to see that you can reach the rear dump and confirm that the manual inflator can be operated and reached easily.

Jill's Opinions

There are no specific men's or women's style wings at this time, but many small women will find standard wings to be extremely wide and large. You may have to get creative when matching a wing size to your weight, buoyancy and accessory gear requirements. Look for something that is large enough but not oversized. I have owned some oversized wings that created undesirable drag. Though some salespeople will steer you away from anything with bungee cords that are used to restrain an unfilled wing, this is a reasonable option to consider. Obviously you would not want to use a wing that had bungees that completely trapped or prevented air from moving around, but lighter duty bungee can be helpful in pulling in that extra flagging fabric in some cases.

Reneé's Opinions

At one time, in my younger years, I had a custom built non-adjustable harness that was amazing. As I've aged, and with more experience, I've transitioned to an adjustable harness that doesn't utilize a backplate. I don't always want that extra weight, certainly topside. I found a backplate, even the shorter ones, are too long for my torso. They dig into my hips and make me a bit top heavy in the water because the doubles sit higher on my back. If I need weighting, I much prefer to add V-weights or weight pockets a little lower on my rig. Tail weights clipped to the bottom of the plate offer a similar adjustment to trim. Years ago I dived a huge (on me) dual bladder wing. I'm never going to dive heavy 104 cft tanks so now I can get away with a smaller wing with a shorter corrugated power inflator hose. I tend to dive with my wing slightly cinched for use with the lighter doubles. I adjust the wings to the lift I need and I'm more streamlined.

Customizing your harness and wing system to fit you can improve your comfort, confidence and performance. Because I now have a backmount harness that fits my body and my needs I'm less hesitant to dive backmount when the situation calls for it.

Women Mentors

Sharon Kegeles - Dive Trainer & Adaptive SCUBA Specialist

"Working with the water for so many years has given me the opportunity to help others understand the power of the water and how it relates to them first as a person, then as a diver. Once they are able to trust the environment, then the magic begins."

Sharon Kegeles, M.S. is an extraordinary woman who despite facing multiple occurrences of discouragement, frustration, and rejection, has always risen to the challenge and has overcome.

Learning to dive, she was berated by her own initial instructor and forced to wear equipment that was ill-fitting. It is because of these experiences and others that she is so gifted and has compassion for all physical ability levels. The experience of adapting all sport and recreation activities to fit the needs of the participant is an important exercise as we learn, reflect and serve others. Most recently her research in the area of accessible tourism has assisted the government of Bonaire as they welcome aging divers and cruise ship tourists to their small island while minimizing common obstacles. That same research has easily transferred into the classroom for the Adapted Physical Activity, Recreation and Sport course taught to nearly 100 university students each year.

Sharon has a multifaceted role at Barry University in Miami Shores, Florida serving as an Assistant Professor in Sport and Exercise Sciences, Coordinator of the Sport Management-Diving Industry B.S. Degree Program and Director of undergraduate programs in Sport and Exercise Sciences. Working with enthusiastic young minds eager to grow as individuals in a demanding academic setting is rewarding. Her students are passionate about the sport as she helps guide them through intensive coursework while offering personal leadership opportunities at every turn. Together along the way they find the key to unlock the door to launch their career. Each one chooses a different path and leaves a lasting impression upon the underclassmen and the industry representatives with whom they network. As sport management professionals with a solid background in business and dedicated to the recreational diving industry, these will be the leaders of the future of the sport we love.

Sharon is a great mentor and her advice to women is that water is the greatest equalizer of strength, agility and speed between people of all ages. "My greatest reward is the serenity and grace that the aquatic world offers me each time I slip underwater."

Sharon has trained professionals from the Nature Foundation of Saint Maarten; the Great White Shark Foundation in Cape Town, Africa; McGill University's Marine Science Outpost in Barbados and other organizations in support of science and diving operations. She advises groups in the training and options for handicapped divers, including London's Access to Marine Conservation for All Program. She was inducted into the Women Divers Hall of Fame in 2006.

Weighting for Backmount Doubles

In technical diving weight may not be an issue since steel tanks and a backplate are often utilized. If you do find you need extra weight, first decide where you need it. For example, if you tend to find your body position to be uncomfortably head down then weighting at the waist or hip level would be appropriate. There are several different ways to add a little weight in the right places. A shorter woman may not have the leg length to properly balance a set of heavier doubles. If that's you, try adding a V-weight between your cylinders and backplate or backpack style harness. The V-weight is a solid block of lead or weight pouches that are affixed to the bolts on the bands of the back-mounted double tanks. The pouch style is equipped with grommets 11 inches apart. Weight pockets are available and are designed to be worn on the waistband. This eats up valuable space and may not be a good option for smaller women. Another option is the "tail weight" which is bolted low to the lower cylinder band bolt. Whichever style you choose, be sure you've not created an entanglement hazard, the weights are attached so they will stay in place and that you have the proper weight you need. The center of balance for a woman is lower than a man's, so trim adjustments can be different too. However you weight yourself, remember that especially in wreck or cave diving, your trim must be horizontal with your feet up so as not to disturb loose silt on the floor.

Weight pockets (above) and tank V-weights (below) are some of the creative options available for weighting double tanks.

Jill's Opinions

I don't need any weight in Florida temperatures but when I head north and add undergarments, I use V-weights on double tanks or non-ditchable weights secured as close as possible to my waistline for balance. Soft weight pockets can be secured to the holes on the edge of a backplate or directly to a sidemount harness. I added weight pockets to the top of the onboard tanks on my rebreather. That helps bring my head down and feet up off the bottom.

Reneé's Opinions

Heavy double tanks cause me to dive in a head down position that I feel is unsafe, so I avoid them. They are also hard for me to safely manage when I try to get out of the water. I like to dive with lighter cylinders but that requires me to wear more weight when diving my neoprene drysuit. I position that weight low and attach secure small concealed weight pockets to the waist belt as far back as I gan get them. I've also been known to put about 2 pounds of soft weight in each leg pocket on my drysuit. With my new Ladies First Santi drysuit I use the DiveRite trim pockets on my harness with about 6 pounds total. Not bad!

Sidemount Tanks

Sidemount diving is becoming very popular, both in the recreational and technical realm. With the tank valves and regulators tucked neatly under your armpits, this style of diving offers more control over gas failures. Carrying one tank to the water at a time is also a great benefit over hefting double tanks.

General Features

Sidemount harnesses help the diver hang their tanks comfortably on the side of their body, parallel with their body. The valves are easily accessible using either hand. A tank cam band is equipped with a large clip that fastens to a rail on a butt plate. The tank valve hangs in a bungee located beneath the arm or is clipped using some other type of bungee/ring/clip device.

Sidemount tanks are often smaller than backmount doubles (above). Sidemount tanks attach to rails on a butt plate (below). Photos: Jill Heinerth

Fit/Sizing

It is crucially important to select the right tanks for sidemount diving. The theory is that your two tanks are perfectly sized for optimized swimming and adequate gas volume. Supplemental aluminum tanks are added for technical applications needing additional gas supplies. Currently, the most popular sidemount tank is a steel LP 85 cft tank. Divers in tropical conditions often use 80 cft aluminum tanks and divers with a lower range requirement love the steel 45 and 55 cft versions.

If you are short, make sure the tank does not hamper your ability to swim comfortably. Try both flutter and frog kicks. You don't want to be kicking your tanks with every fin stroke.

Materials

Steel tanks sit squarely on the diver and do not tend to shift significantly in their fore/aft trim as they are depleted. Aluminum tanks shift significantly, getting lighter in the base as

Sidemount technique is preferred by many who would rather manage one tank at a time. Here Jill Heinerth is seen with her favorite steel LP77 tanks. Photo: Gene Page

Sidemount tanks are routinely donned in the water, although it is quite easy to get fully dressed on board a boat as long as you have practiced getting ready in confined spaces. Photo: Jill Heinerth

they empty. For this reason, the diver may need to modify the lower tank connection points so there are two different clip locations. At the beginning of the dive, your tank may sit parallel with your body when clipped to the butt rail. However, as the tank drops below 2000 psi/135 bar, you may feel a shift that makes the lower end of the tank begin to rise. At this time you can re-clip the lower end of the tank to a D-ring on the front of the waistband to bring it down again.

Special Considerations

Having two separate tanks means you can carry one at a time to the boat or the water. If you are a boat diver, confirm the captain will support sidemount diving. You need to remember to take only your share of boat space and be very proficient in clipping tanks without taking up the whole boat. In many cases you can easily clip the top clip securely and then jump in and fix the rest in the water. If you put your gear near the back of the vessel at the transom, then you won't have to trip over anyone else to get to the water. Alternatively, the captain may encourage you to hang your tanks on a gear line and dress in the water. This is a great solution for people with back issues. Whatever technique works for you should be well practiced so that you can work efficiently and independently on the vessel.

Jill's Opinions

As I mentioned earlier, I have a great bias toward using sidemount configuration. I believe I am capable of better self-management of emergencies. For smaller women, I think this is also a great solution. Carrying a set of double manifolded tanks is tough for the strongest of us. There is no reason why you can't use sidemount and ease the stress on your back and muscles.

Sidemount configuration requires patience, an open mind and a good experienced instructor who understands that each person requires unique creative solutions. You can rarely come up with an optimized solution without the help of an experienced instructor tweaking the details in the water.

Although I am a tall girl, I love steel LP77s and LP71s. They are short and easy to carry to the water. They don't interfere with my kick and offer plenty of volume for most of my dives. Steel 85s are my second choice.

Reneé's Opinions

Sidemount is my gear configuration of choice. I recognize that it is a tool just like backmount, no-mount or a rebreather. I choose sidemount because walking to and from the water, not to mention climbing in and out of sinkholes (stairs or not), can be very challenging and even dangerous. So from a safety standpoint I'll choose sidemount every time. It is very easy for me to rig my sidemount cylinders, put them on a hand truck, haul them to the water then lower them in one at a time. After having my ACL replaced and having an injured cervical spine I'm much more interested in protecting my body than I am proving I can carry heavy cylinders.

I prefer steel LP 85s and I can dive them easily wet or dry. My next best option is the timeless aluminum 80.

Sidemount Rigs

Sidemount rigs were originally cobbled together by divers in garages, but the last 10 years have seen great advancements in commercially available sidemount harnesses and air cell systems.

General Features

Belt systems were some of the first methods to be used for sidemount diving and are the easiest to configure. Though several designs exist, the basic structure includes a harness and waist strap system that allows cylinders to be slung on the sides using D-ring attachment points on the waist or rear, via extensions, while the top of the cylinders are held in place with a stretchy bungee of some type. These harnesses generally do not include buoyancy compensators but they may be added as an after-market modification. Belt harnesses are the most streamlined of all of the current sidemount systems when used in their basic configuration, with lightweight aluminum cylinders in shallow water.

Other early sidemount configurations were made from highly modified open water diving BCDs. The foundation of the first North American systems were larger capacity buoyancy "stab" jackets that were modified by incorporating web

The Hollis line of SMS50, 75 and 100 harnesses are very popular. Each unit has a greater lift capacity than the previous model, allowing for more tanks and accessory gear. Photo: Robert McClellan

harnesses, mounting plates, brackets, D-rings, clips, inner tubes, and bungee cords.

Purpose-built modern systems offer many advantages over primitive homebuilt units, With different options for lift and streamlining, commercially available sidemount systems can handle many different cylinder options. There are some differences in lifting capacities between various models, so the basic principles in buoyancy capacity vs. profile size may play a part in the purchasing decision.

Helen Farr is wearing a custom designed webbed Farrworld harness while demonstrating the original intent for the configuration - to fit in small spaces within caves (above). Seen from above, a sidemount unit is streamlined and comfortable in any environment (below). Photos: Jill Heinerth

If a diver expects to carry large steel cylinders or multiple cylinders for stage diving, then a high volume, larger profile system may be the right choice. If the diver plans to work in extremely confined spaces, or with medium sized cylinders, then one of the lower profile, lower volume systems would be in order. There is no way to avoid the basic physics of the fact that if lift is increased, then so is the profile.

Fit/Sizing

Sidemount units vary in size and lift capacity and there will be some manufacturer's solutions that simply won't fit your body. To date, the only manufacturer who can custom fit individual parts of a sidemount harness is Dive Rite. They have a modular design that can interchange shoulder straps, backpads, and other parts. If you are really small, this might be a good solution.

Special Considerations

Once a system has been purchased, the next and most important step is proper adjustment. This step should be made with the assistance of an experienced sidemount instructor. Proper adjustment can be tedious in the first dive or two, but once the adjustments are made properly, the rest of the system including cylinder placement, accessory placement, buoyancy and trim all fall easily into place. Without assistance with this first step, the diver is in for a long and frustrating learning curve. More than other gear configurations, fitting of sidemount gear may come down to micro adjustments that make significant changes in trim. These micro adjustments need to be done in the water, where the observing instructor can shift D-rings and move straps to arrive at optimal trim. Once your rig is properly adjusted, it will be completely personalized. A diver with different body morphology is as unlikely to fit in your harness as you are hers. For this reason, it is rare that divers will use rental sidemount rigs or loan out their kit. Most instructors require divers to own their personal equipment, unless they are taking part in try-dive scenarios as a part of a purchasing decision.

Men's Versus Women's Styles

To date, all sidemount rigs are designed as unisex devices. That means you need to pay special attention to the length of the torso, width of shoulder straps and location of the waist. You may need to add a chest strap to cinch in the shoulders. The device should fit you like a parachute harness— snug and secure. If the unit is not form-fitting then the tanks will shift around when you dive, affecting your center of balance and throwing you off good trim.

Jill's Opinions

Having started sidemount diving with an old open water Sherwood BCD, I recognize how far this technology has come. I would never go back to a homebuilt version. Sidemount harnesses incorporate wings that place the lift where you need it— over your hips. If you try to convert an old wing for this purpose, your trim will be off, likely putting you in head up position dragging your feet across the bottom. There is simply no replacement for getting the right gear. Sell your old doubles rig and invest in a properly designed sidemount rig from a manufacturer who has worked for years to evolve their product. Find a patient instructor who understands that a woman's center

When sidemount tanks are trimmed properly, they are almost completely hidden when viewing the diver head on. Regulators are neatly stowed and pressure gauges are a simple glance away. Cave diver Khrista Zand shows how to do it well. Photo: Jill Heinerth

of balance is different than a man's and who enjoys the customization of helping you perfect your gear. If all their students struggle to use identical solutions, they likely are not open minded enough to help properly fit a female sidemount diver.

I use Hollis sidemount rigs. The SMS50 is an awesome, modest lift unit that fits me like a glove and is a terrific solution for many smaller women. I use the SMS100 when diving with multiple tanks. The new SMS75 seems to be the best middle ground for lift and flexibility in tank choices. Plus, you've got to love the red accent color!

Reneé's Opinions

I first started sidemount diving during an expedition with The Cambrian Foundation in Mexico in 2000. I ordered my Dive Rite TransPac sidemount harness and it came in pieces in a bag which at that time was daunting to me. I was a human mannequin standing in the living room overlooking the sea as the guys transformed a bag of stainless hardware and webbing into my first sidemount rig. As a small woman, I think Dive Rite is and always has been the only technical gear manufacturer that could accommodate my weird dimensions while providing impeccable customer service. To their chagrin at times I bet, I have them on speed dial.

With shorter arms it can be very difficult to reach the rear tank attachment rails on sidemount units. Fortunately they can be adjusted to accommodate your personal reach on many models. It is critical that you can remove and replace your own sidemount cylinders underwater if needed. On the surface, the challenge can be trying to attach the cylinders in water too deep to stand with the wing fully or partially inflated. There is the obvious risk of dropping the cylinder, damaging the equipment, the environment or another diver. Some sidemount divers first attach the cylinder to a front attachment point for security. The rear of the cylinder can then be easily clipped to the rail by leaning back. Then you can snug the upper part of the cylinders with the bungees. Find what works for you while standing, while floating on the surface and when underwater and practice.

Marissa Lasso demonstrates clean use of the "bottom-up" inflator connection which is more protected than the "over the shoulder" style standard on most diving wings. Photo: Jill Heinerth

Your wing, like any wing or "bladder," is based on the cylinder size you'll be diving. For example, if you plan to dive steel 85s with 2 stages in a wetsuit, then an extremely low profile minimalist design wing may not offer enough lift and wouldn't be your best option. A minimalist design could be an excellent choice if diving aluminum 80s. When selecting a wing always check the manufacturer's specifications and confirm that the lift it will provide is compatible with the lift you need.

Historically, the power inflator has run off of the left shoulder in nearly every style BCD or wing. Some manufacturers are now offering an option to have the inflator connected to the lower portion of the wing. The rationale is that the chest area is now clean, and which makes the back up regulator more available and accessible. Although this is a viable option, be aware of the cons of this design. One is muscle memory. If you've been diving very long, you've trained yourself to find the power inflator on your upper left chest regardless of the gear configuration. Switching to this alternate method starts that learning process over. It will be important to retrain yourself until you are "unconsciously competent," meaning that reaching for your inflator in this new location becomes "second nature" and you do not have to think about it.

Weighting for Sidemount

Weighting can be a little more tricky in a sidemount configuration. Depending on your exposure protection you may find you are properly weighted by the cylinders alone just like diving backmounted doubles. However, in sidemount there's no metal backplate to provide negative ballast. If you find yourself needing more weight you might have to get creative. One option is trim weight pouches. These pouches are often available by the same manufacturer as your sidemount rig and they can show you where to place them. If your pouches have a Velcro closure be sure they are secured so they stay attached. If you are a small woman in a small harness you might not have enough room for pockets. Pockets come in different sizes so find what works for you. Another option is to use steel cylinders. Some divers will put a small amount of weight on the harness shoulder straps to help with trim in the event that their shoulders are high and feet are low. Another idea is to put weight on the cylinders themselves. If you choose this technique, bear in mind that if you have to remove a cylinder while diving it could be more difficult to manage when negative.

Trim is critical in sidemount. The cylinders ride lower on the body than they do in backmount. This can cause your feet to be a little negative which is not ideal. You can adjust the tank bands to move the position of the cylinders on your sides up or down. If you find you have the cylinders in the right place but are still a little feet heavy have a look at your fins. If you have heavy rubber fins consider using fins that are a little lighter.

Afterthought: Jill

Steel 85s or 77s work well for me. When I dive in cold water, I add weight to interior ballast pockets in my harness and sometimes use a special backplate attachment that accepts weight in a series of pockets. The device attaches to the harness on the 11-inch spaced holes with book screws.

Reneé's Opinions

I almost always dive my steel 85s. They are a little long for me but the weight is just right. For me, aluminum cylinders with my neoprene drysuit are out of the question. However, in a wetsuit or my Santi Ladies First drysuit, I really like them. I use trim weights some of the time and almost always a 4-pound drop weight that I place just inside the cave at the beginning of the continuous guideline. This way I can pick it up on my way out of the cave and I will have enough weight to maintain a safe depth for my shallow safety or decompression stops.

Women Mentors

Rhonda Moniz - ROV Pilot and Underwater Technology Specialist

Rhonda Moniz decided she wanted a career in diving when she was eight years old. At her grandmother's house she stumbled on an underwater book series by Jacques Yves Cousteau. She recalls sitting on the floor, captivated by the pictures of the divers in their dive gear swimming underwater. At that time she also went to see the movie *Jaws*. That clinched it. To this day she is still fascinated by sharks and works creating a world that is more interested in shark conservation than shark decimation.

Back in the day there were not a whole lot of role models for young girls. Yet, Rhonda got certified as a Junior Open Water diver when she was 12 years old. After high school she attended college and earned a business management degree. While working in Rhode Island as one of the lead dive instructors during the early 90s, she was hired by a university to assist in scientific diving operations. She pursued further training in a number of underwater technologies including surface supply diving, underwater cinematography, and Remotely Operated Vehicles (ROV). She has also been promoting the use of marine technology in underwater forensics. She returned to school for a graduate degree in documentary production and has worked on a number of projects for PBS, and the Discovery Channel among others.

Some of her favorite work experiences are as an ROV pilot in Turkey and Greece on board the E/V Nautilus with Dr. Robert Ballard. The focus in Turkey was on underwater archeology studying ancient shipwrecks. In Greece her team studied underwater volcanos. While working with Dr. Ballard she learned she was his first female ROV pilot.

Rhonda suggests that the power of networking is important to recognize. She is often asked to give talks to young girls focusing on science, technology, engineering, and mathematics (STEM). During those engagements she reminds kids to "never, never, never give up," and "90 percent of success is showing up!"

Networking includes joining marine related groups, volunteering or getting internships as ways to introduce yourself and show them what you can do. There have been times in the past when she contacted an organization to see if there were any job openings and was disappointed to find there was not. Instead of giving up, she asked if she could volunteer one day per week. This led to more than one organization creating a position for her.

Rhonda's career as a professional in the diving and marine technology field spans over 25 years. Things are very different now than they used to be with regard to women working in the industry. She doesn't feel that there were as many opportunities as there are now. This is a great time for young women interested in careers in the underwater world.

Photos courtesy of Rhonda Moniz.

Regulators for Technical Diving

The type of regulator you choose is based on preference and the type of diving you'll be doing. Confirm that the manufacturer's specifications for your regulators are compatible with the environment you will be diving in. Technical diving regulators should meet CE EN250 performance requirements. They should be maintained by an authorized service technician at least annually and more often if you are extremely active. If you dive in cold water, the regulator should be designed for cold water use. The first stage should be equipped with a DIN style fitting. The second stage should be comfortable in your mouth with a mouthpiece that fits and does not cause jaw fatigue.

A consideration in backmount doubles is regulator hose length. Traditionally a 5-7 foot (1.5 - 2m) hose has been part of the kit for the backmount diver and a shorter hose for the backup regulator. If you're a smaller female, the 7-foot hose may be a bit overwhelming and difficult to manage so consider a 5-foot hose. You can test to see if this hose is a good length for you by simply standing up while you are fully geared. Gently lower your 5-foot (1.5m) long hose to the ground and if the regulator touches the ground you are probably good to go! If you're planning a scooter dive or a dive in tighter passage, then a 7-foot (2m) hose is probably still the safest method in case of an air share necessity. Both regulators should be secured to you in some fashion either by a necklace or a clip so they don't dangle risking entanglement or damage to your equipment or the environment.

Ensure your regulator will be ready for cold water diving if that is in your plans. Photo: Jill Heinerth

Jill's Opinions

Many divers make a slow transition from recreational to technical diving without consideration for their regulators. What served well in 130 feet/40 meters of water may not perform adequately for deep trimix dives. Check the manufacturer's specifications closely to ensure your regulator is sufficient for deep or cold water diving performance. Also ensure that your gear is regularly serviced by a reputable source that can ensure top performance when you need it most.

Reneé's Opinions

This is life support equipment. Early on in my technical diving I chose to have the proper regulator for the dive I was doing. I use a combination of a clip and a necklace to secure my regulators so they don't dangle. For years I struggled with a 7 foot (2m) hose. A few months ago, I made an informed decision to switch to a 5-foot (1.5m) hose for most situations. I can deploy and stow it much easier which makes me safer and I'm less distracted. I also have a shorter primary regulator hose to help with streamlining.

Accessory Gear

There is a lot of additional accessory equipment that you will use for technical diving. Much of that gear is quite universal, such as lights, delayed surface marker buoys (DSMBs), reels, spools and cutting tools. What is unique for a woman is sometimes finding a place to stow that gear. If you have a small waist and short torso, there is not a lot of territory left on those straps to secure gear in a way that some standardized agency training might prefer. You'll have to be creative to find alternative places that you can reach and don't dangle. You can use suit pockets, accessory pockets and other creative clip points to put things away. If you justify your choice of an alternative method that is safe, provides easy access to deploy and stow and does not create drag or entanglement hazard, then there is no reason why you should not use that method. Be prepared to describe to your instructor why your technique works for you and tell others to back off when they try to reconfigure your gear for you.

Technical Diving Lights

Proper lighting is important to a technical diver. A canister primary light is traditionally mounted to the waistband of backmounted doubles with a long cord attached to the light head. For a woman this may be a challenge if your torso is short because one end digs in your ribs and the other end in your hip. If you choose this method to secure your canister light and are having difficulty, consider a smaller canister and battery that still offers the burn time you need. Or,

Light & Motion Sola Tech 600 light. Photo: Courtesy Light & Motion

find another spot to mount the canister. Some primary lights have a twist on/off option on the light head itself. With this design, you won't need to reach the canister top and can be stowed in nearly any location that still offers streamlining. If the cord is too long, it can be customized. The light head may be carried in your hand, but it is difficult to hold a light and maneuver using with the same hand. Secure the light to a hand mount of some style. If you are a woman with small hands you may find sizing a challenge. But, soft hand

Kristine Rae Olmsted uses a canister light neatly mounted to her sidemount harness. She wraps any excess cord length around her arm and mounts backup lights to her helmet. Photo: Jill Heinerth

mounts can be adjusted and customized to fit your own hand. This can be a great option because your light is secure and you can still use your hand to maneuver or grasp. Some manufacturers have designed primary lights that are completely cordless. Some of these lights may be a bit large for a small woman's hands. Yet, recent battery and technology improvements have produced incredible small lights with lengthy burn times for technical diving applications. If possible, try a light before you buy to ensure it is comfortable and the light head is neutral underwater.

Canister dive lights are usually provided with a single cord but sometimes have an option of an E/O connector. This connector allows the light to be plugged and unplugged underwater. With this option you can switch to a different light head or a different battery underwater giving you more options. This is a great application if you anticipate the need to switch to a brighter light for video, for example. If your drysuit has a heated undergarment you can unplug your light head then connect the battery to the connector for the undergarment. The light head can be stored separately in a protective travel case with an E/O cord. If you aren't planning to switch then a standard cord may be your best bet to keep things simple.

Now, where to put backup lights? You can put them in a pocket, a pouch or clip to your harness or helmet. Just make sure you lights are streamlined and can be accessed and replaced easily. Lanyards are really not considered safe in technical diving due to the entanglement hazard with cave line, fishing line or even your own gear. Replace a lanyard with an appropriate size and type of clip for the application.

Should you have rechargeable or disposable batteries in your back up lights? Consider one of each. Disposable batteries will die out very slowly offering at least some light while rechargeable batteries will die out sharply when a cutoff voltage is reached. Don't mix new batteries with partially used ones and never mix disposable and rechargeable batteries in a light. In

Rechargeable or disposable batteries, twist or switch actuation, materials, construction, weight and buoyancy will all affect your choice of backup lights.

order to improve the overall life of NiMH batteries, charge them monthly even if you're not using them. It goes without saying that you should confirm that your batteries, whether rechargeable or not, will last the length of your dive or longer. The recommendation is that the burn time should be one and a half times the length of your dive. If you aren't sure how much life your batteries have in them it's best to use a fresh set.

Jill's Opinions

In general, I like to stow backup lights in my thigh pockets or on my helmet. My 12-watt Light Monkey primary light is slipped onto the waistband of my backmounted doubles set and locked in place with a weight belt buckle with the release folded towards my body for security. When diving sidemount, I prefer to butt mount my canister light very low, underneath the crotch strap and below the curve of my bottom. This is extremely streamlined for small spaces. The cord is routed up my hip, under the waistband and under the chest strap, emerging above the chest strap to run down my arm to a soft adjustable Finn Light hand mount. The light is easily activated by twisting the head.

Recently I have switched to the Light & Motion Sola Tech 600 light. Extremely small and lightweight, this mounts comfortably on the hand and needs no canister or cord. The burn time is fantastic and the light can be powered up and down to conserve if necessary. Travel is easy due to its light weight and compact charger.

Reneé's Opinions

When diving backmounted doubles, I store my canister light angled on my waistband so it doesn't dig anywhere. The switch is on the canister and I can reach it just fine. In sidemount, I clip it to the back of my rig. I'm currently rethinking canister placement and desire the switch to be on the light head so I don't have to worry about reaching the switch. I sometimes use a soft hand mount for my primary light head. I bought the small size, but it was still too big so the manufac-

Reneé testing the Halcyon EON light with adjustable handle. Photo: Jill Heinerth

turer made it even smaller for me. I really enjoy having the soft mount when pulling through high flow in caves. My hands are small and I can get a better grip on the rock when not having to grasp the light head. I can remove it easily from the mount when needed. Backup lights go in my drysuit pockets. If I'm diving a wetsuit I utilize a removable thigh pocket. One of my primary lights has a WetMate E/O connector. Several times during exploration in very small passage, my light cord has gotten snagged on a rock and unplugged itself. Due to the nature of the dive and in zero visibility I quickly found myself alone and in the dark. It was merely an inconvenience and I'm thankful it indeed came back on once reconnected.

Handling Longer Dives— Urination

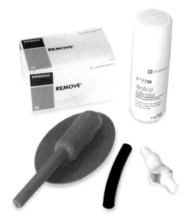

At some point in your technical or boat diving career, you will reach the point where proper hydration has left you needing to pee. Proper hydration is important and so is finding a comfortable, private way to void.

The oldest trick in the book is to wear adult diapers. Most women will share some good tactics if you are not too afraid to ask. First, you need some serious absorbency. The amount of volume you will pee can be significant. Nobody want diapers to leak, so you can try wearing them under a pair of bicycle style shorts—

Components of the She-P System.

without or without the chamois padding. The shorts keep everything in place and minimize leaks. They also disguise the diapers if you have to peel out of your undergarments on a boat. For really long missions, add a big absorbent pad in the middle to capture even more volume. The most important thing is to pee slowly. If

you just let loose, you may be more likely to leak. If you urinate slowly, it gives time for the absorbent material to wick up the moisture.

There are at least two products in the market that act as external catheters to route urine out of the suit through a P-valve. The popular She-P is a silicone device which is glued in place. It takes some training and shaving for efficient use. It is not for everyone, but it does allow you stand on the back of the boat and pee like a man. The She-Wee from Custom Divers varies slightly on that theme. There is no glue required. A funnel-shape latex g-string device is worn and hooked up to the quick release tubing leading to the P-valve in the suit.

Components of the Custom Divers She-Wee System (above). The urination device is connected to tubing with a quick release mechanism. That tubing leads to the port that must be installed into the dry suit. You can do it yourself or get a professional to cut the hole and glue the port into the leg (below).

General Features

P-valve systems come in two styles: balanced and unbalanced. In the unbalanced version, a screw valve on the outside of the suit is opened by the diver when they want to urinate. It is closed again when completed. The balanced version uses an additional chamber tube inside the suit to equalize pressure with the tubing with ambient pressure. In either case, a one way check may also prevent spillage when disconnection occurs.

P-valve outlets are easily installed in drysuits. Most kits come with instructions to do this at home yourself. If it makes you nervous, have the valve installed when you purchase the suit or take it to a repair technician that can stomach cutting a hole in your expensive suit.

A hole of about one-half inch diameter is cut in the suit and a valve is glued in place from the inside and outside. You have to mark the location that you want the valve. Put on your suit, then choose a leg and pick a spot slightly to the inside of the front of your leg. The P-valve can be a snag point if it is too far in front or too far around the outside of your leg. If it is too high inside the leg, it will be uncomfortable and might hit your other leg when swimming.The region around a P-valve can be prone to wear. If you have the ability, double up the fabric around the edge of the installation to protect from stress and abrasion.

The plumbing for the valve is included in a kit and has a universal quick release. When you get into your suit, pull the tubing up so you don't get it caught in the leg of the suit. The She-P tubing routes out through the bottom of the zipper in your dry suit undergarments. If your undergarments don't have a zipper, you will have to cut an access hole in them. Once you are comfortably settled in your suit you simply snap together the two ends of the quick release. Before you get in the water, prime the hose by peeing a little. As long as there is fluid in the hose you likely won't get a squeeze, although this can occur with kinked tubing. Take note of any crotch strap buckles to make sure they are not directly compressing the She-P or She-Wee. A crotch strap might help hold things in place, but a buckle could bruise you.

Fit/Sizing

The She-P comes in two sizes. The She-Wee device is one size that buckles into several sizes of shorts that come with it. Many women can find a fit in either device, but in many cases, women still experience leakage or squeezes. Some divers choose to wear a light absorbency diaper to catch leaks.

Materials

The devices are made from silicone and latex and need to be properly and regularly cleaned. There is a risk of genitourinary infections if you do not take proper care of the gear.[3] Vigorous washing with soap and water may be adequate, but if the device needs deeper cleaning of the narrow tubing, then a medical device washing solution is recommended. If you are a rebreather diver, a sanitizing solution used for your rebreather may do the trick.

Jill's Opinions

On an expedition where my dive missions spanned over 20 hours, it was the number one question I was asked. No pun intended. It is an important question. I have installed P-valves in all my drysuits, but still have not found the perfect solution that is comfortable, consistently reliable and easy to use. Shaving is not a viable option for me in an expeditionary setting. The inconvenience and discomfort cause by repeated razor rash can be a lot worse than the perceived embarrassment of wearing diapers or incontinence pants.

If you think you want to use diapers, ensure that your custom drysuit is measured with that in mind. If your suit is too tight in the hips, you will not be able to accommodate diapers. A snug suit will cramp your swimming style and comfort. If your dive duration is excessive, try adding an extra absorbent layer such as a feminine protection pad or part of a baby diaper. Some baby diapers/nappies are equipped with small absorbent beads that only expand when wet and are comfortable and discrete if unused.

Reneé's Opinions

I have a P-valve installed in my drysuit and I have tried one of the devices with no luck. I use diapers – big old man diapers. I wear stretchy shorts on top and my undergarments over those. It's easy to be discreet about putting them on or taking them off, though in the technical realm, divers are not bothered by the sight of a diaper going in the trash.

---

[3] Genitourinary infection and barotrauma as complications of P-valve use in drysuit divers. Richard Harris, *Diving and Hyperbaric Medicine*, Volume 39, No. 4, December 2009.

Rebreathers

Rebreathers have actually been around longer than open circuit SCUBA, but their advancement into the world of sport diving is quite recent. Quality manufactured products are now available for both recreational and technical divers.

Reneé Power with the Hollis Explorer Intelligent SCR. Photo: Pam Wooten

General Features

Open circuit SCUBA is inefficient and time limited. Much of every exhaled breath from a SCUBA tank is wasted. Our bodies only use a very small portion of the oxygen component of air or nitrox. We metabolize a tiny bit of the available oxygen and expend the rest into the water column in a stream of bubbles. A rebreather is designed to recapture all or part of that exhaled breath and recycle as much as possible for the diver to use again. As a result, we are offered many advantages over traditional SCUBA, such as a longer bottom time per unit of gas, reduced bubbling that might frighten away marine life, as well as increased warmth.

It sounds like a simple enough concept, but rebreathers perform some other important tasks. Each exhaled breath contains carbon dioxide, which can rapidly build up and cause our bodies distress. The rebreather has to "clean" the gas and remove carbon dioxide before sending it back to the diver. It also has to make up the lost volume of oxygen that was metabolized by the diver. It's a balancing act. The rebreather has to predictably and repeatedly add small amounts of oxygen and remove carbon dioxide to keep the life support environment optimized and safe for a diver to breathe.

There are many types of rebreathers from fully manual to electronically controlled.

Semi Closed Circuit Rebreathers (SCR)

Semi Closed Circuit Rebreathers are generally simple in form and function. In this type of rebreather, only one tank of gas is used onboard. Depending on the design, the gas may enter the breathing loop in a number of different ways. It may flow continuously, be injected based on the breathing rate of the diver or added intelligently by an electronic system as required.

Carrying only a single gas, an SCR may offer a leaner package and simplicity for recreational rebreather divers. Photo: Pam Wooten

When a diver's exertion rate is high and when a low percentage of oxygen is carried in the tank, then a greater flow of gas must be provided in order to keep oxygen partial pressure at an acceptable level. With more inflowing gas, the diver or unit may vent bubbles at a greater rate, resulting in faster gas use. If a higher percentage of oxygen is carried in the onboard tank or if the exertion of the diver is lower, then venting of bubbles may be reduced and the gas may be used at a slower rate in some models. In SCRs, depth should never exceed the safe partial pressure of the gas in the supply tank.

SCRs are not common in the technical end of rebreather diving because they do not offer the decompression advantage that fully closed circuit rebreathers present for a diver.

Kim Smith, former owner of KISS Rebreathers, dives on a small wreck in the Dominican Republic. Smith plays a key role in the operation of the rebreather safety organization, RESA. Photo: Jill Heinerth

The method of gas addition helps to describe different models of SCRs:

Active-addition – a rebreather gas-addition system that actively injects a continuous stream of gas into the breathing loop (such as a constant-mass flow valve in certain kinds of semi-closed rebreathers). Imagine breathing in and out of a paper bag. If a stream of continuous fresh gas is fed in to that paper bag, then some will be inhaled and some will bleed out around the edges. If you breathe fast and metabolize more oxygen molecules, there may be less gas bleeding out of the bag. If you breathe slowly, then more gas will be wasted and vented.

Passive-addition – a gas addition system utilized by some SCRs to passively inject gas into the breathing loop; usually achieved by a mechanical valve that opens in response to a collapsed bellows or drop in breathing loop gas pressure. In this case, imagine that as you breathe in and out of the paper bag, you slowly deplete the volume due to metabolizing the oxygen in the bag. When the volume drops in the bag, it gets harder to breathe. Passive addition valves will be triggered to flow with a drop in volume in the bag.

Electronically Monitored mSCR — a mechanical SCR with electronic monitoring. In this case, electronics are used to inform the diver of PO_2 as well as provide warnings and status updates, however the gas control is manually controlled by the diver.

Semi-Closed Intelligent – an electronic gas addition system utilized by the newest class of eSCRs to intelligently inject gas into the breathing loop when a drop in partial pressure warrants an addition. In this way they can match changing metabolism better than their mechanical counterparts. In this example, an oxygen monitoring and control device has been added to the system. When the PO_2 drops, fresh gas is added to maintain a suitable floating setpoint (desired PO_2 in the breathing loop) to optimize gas use and other consumables and to adjust for changing exertion (oxygen consumption) rates of the diver.

Gas also flows into the bag automatically if a pressure drop warrants. A failsafe mode reverts the eSCR to the active addition mode in the event of total failure.

By their nature, semi-closed circuit rebreathers make more bubbles than closed-circuit rebreathers. They are designed to vent in order to make room for higher partial pressure gas that brings the PO_2 up. Active-addition style SCRs make more bubbles than either passive or intelligent styles and all rebreathers will vent bubbles upon ascent. A valve called an Over Pressurization Valve (OPV) is fitted onto all rebreathers. Whenever the volume of gas in the breathing loop exceeds a given level, such as upon ascent, then bubbles will vent through the OPV.

Closed Circuit Rebreathers (CCR)

CCRs are the most popular type of unit for technical divers. They offer the greatest decompression advantage since they create a virtual mixing station on your back. As a result, they have their own inherent risks.

Rebreathers revolutionize your diving experience. Making few bubbles you will silently glide through the underwater world without frightening marine life. Photos: Jill Heinerth

In this type of rebreather, two bottles of gas are supplied onboard. One tank is filled with pure oxygen and the other tank is filled with diluent gas. When you start diving on this type of rebreather, the diluent tank will likely be filled with air. As you descend in the water column and the surrounding pressure increases, collapsing the counterlungs, an automatic diluent valve will open and diluent gas will flow into the breathing loop. While descending, the PO_2 naturally rises from increased pressure and you are also metabolizing oxygen. You may reach your target depth before you need more oxygen molecules in the loop.

When the PO_2 drops, then a valve is triggered either manually by the diver or automatically through an electronics system. A tiny addition of oxygen brings the breathing mix back up to a safe PO_2. Generally, the oxygen injection occurs in a location ahead of the scrubber. In the scrubber, the gas mixes and homogenizes and is cleansed of carbon dioxide. When it exits the scrubber, it passes by one or more oxygen sensors. The PO_2 is displayed in the computer handset and triggers the primary controller (in an electronic rebreather) to add oxygen as required.

As your dive commences and you metabolize oxygen, more oxygen will be needed to make up the balance. Further injections of oxygen will be triggered by the diver or the electronics depending on the type of rebreather.

In a CCR, oxygen is added judiciously and as a result, there is less likelihood of having too much gas in the breathing loop causing a situation where gas is vented as bubbles into the water column (if you remain at a stable depth). If the rebreather is piloted well and the diver has a good mask seal, then bubbles will only vent on ascent (including small rises in the dive profile) as the gas volume in the breathing loop expands.

The act of adding oxygen in CCRs happens in a number of ways. In a manual rebreather, the diver closely watches their handset, which informs them about the PO_2 inside the breathing loop. When PO_2 drops below their target setpoint, the diver pushes a button that causes oxygen to flow into the loop. Careful and constant monitoring is required. This type of rebreather is also referred to as a Diver Controlled CCR or dcCCR. Electronic CCRs allow the diver to choose a PO_2 setpoint. The onboard computer monitors PO_2 and adds oxygen when the PO_2 drops below the chosen setpoint. Most eCCRs are equipped with a manual addition valve and can function just like a diver controlled CCR if desired.

Cave diver, Amy Ferguson wearing her Revo CCR in North Florida. Photo: Jill Heinerth

Fit/Sizing

Rebreathers come in various sizes depending on brand and features. Some rebreathers are better suited to fitting a variety of individuals than others. The counterlungs on a rebreather are sized to fit a range of lung volumes. A small woman will feel overwhelmed by a pair of large counterlungs. Something smaller will be easier to dive and will swim more efficiently in the water. Likewise, a very large person should be sure that their countlerungs offer sufficient volume for comfortable breathing, especially at maximum exertion. Harnesses on rebreathers can often be customized or switched out for your favorite backplate/wing combination. If this is not the case, check to see if the standard configuration will fit you well.

A Discover Rebreather session or pool demonstration will help you find a unit that fits well, but don't make a purchase decision simply based on fit. The features of rebreathers vary greatly and you should search for one that fits your diving well into the future.

Special Considerations

When you ask someone, "Which model is the best rebreather?" they will undoubtedly describe the one they own. Divers develop a strong attachment to their shiny, new and significant investment, and are unlikely to point out any failings in their gear. They may even be right. Their rebreather may indeed be the best rebreather… for them.

The bottom line is that the last decade of statistics shows us that the actual equipment brand or rebreather type does not seem to be a factor in causing accidents. Best available stats show us that there are no more accidents on one particular brand than another based on ratios to the number of units sold. The same appears to be true when we look at manual versus electronic units. That means, the most important decision you can make is not *which* rebreather you buy, but rather *how* you will use it.

There are a lot of things that should affect your purchase decision, even before you start to look at individual features.

Lynn and Bruce Partridge, of Shearwater Research in Canada, are perhaps the largest manufacturer of rebreather controllers and third-party devices in the world. They launched the business in their Vancouver apartment and have grown exponentially over the years (above). Photo: Jill Heinerth Learn where you will need to send your unit for service. It may factor in to your buying decision (below). Photo: Leon Scamahorn

Third-Party Testing— Remember the little red and back circles in the Consumer Reports Magazine that highlight faults in various household products? We don't have that for rebreathers. Much of the manufacturing process is proprietary and secretive. Third-party testing and validation ensures that quality control standards have been applied in the manufacturing process and that industry-agreed-upon safety standards are met consistently. You should insist on seeing CE EN14143:2013 or equivalent test data for work of breathing, oxygen tracking, canister duration and other factors.

Portability— If you are planning to travel with your unit, will it fit within baggage weight standards for your carrier? Is it modular? Is it common enough that you can find tanks and other parts at a vacation destination? Is there international support for your rebreather?

Instruction— You'll want to look for an instructor even before you buy a unit. The instructor base for many rebreathers is still rather small. It is important to learn from a trusted, experienced and current instructor. The manufacturer may offer a "qualified" list of instructors that they recommend and that have a proven background and currency (frequent diving as opposed to dollars!) enough to gain their recommendation. You may need to budget for travel to an instructor's home base in order to get introductory or advanced training.

Support— Having local support and role modeling from dive shops or experienced locals on a particular unit is worth its weight in gold. If everyone in your dive club owns one type of rebreather, then you should give it a hard look. Having role models, spare parts and dive boat support is very helpful.

Service— Do a little research on the manufacturer and their support centers. Can you get local service or do you have to ship internationally for repair? Does the manufacturer or support center offer good customer service, timely repairs and reasonable warranty coverage? Will shipping delays cause you to miss a season of planned dives?

Megan Cook prepares her Hollis PRISM2 rebreather while training during her tenure as the Rolex Our World Underwater Scholar. Photo: Jill Heinerth

Self Service— If you are a traveler, are there easy things that you can repair or replace or are the parts and tools all proprietary and complex? Is this important to you? Some rebreathers can be serviced by local CCR dive shops but others must be sent to the manufacturer. Some people want to be able to quickly replace sub-components on an expedition and others may never want to self-service anything.

History— How long has the manufacturer been in business? Is the business reliant on a single person as the company brain trust or is there a larger entity behind the brand? When software engineer Will Smithers tragically died in a helicopter crash, his programming brilliance was also lost. His intellectual property powered a number of early CCRs. You'll want to learn a little bit about the manufacturer of your rebreather and whether you feel like the company is stable and robust and likely to be around for the life of your purchase.

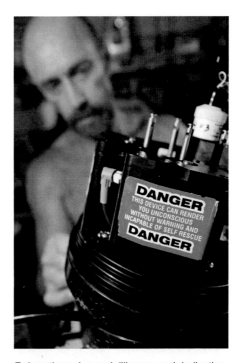

Budget— Your budget will affect your choice of rebreather. You may want to own the top of the line technical rebreather that makes coffee at the dive site, but have to look realistically at a lower price point. You need to budget for the unit itself, proper instruction, consumables and regular maintenance. Don't blow the budget on the unit itself and then cut corners on replacing sensors. If you don't have the finances to support meticulous maintenance, then don't buy the unit in the first place.

Availability of Consumables— You will regularly use batteries in your rebreather. Some are rechargeable and some require unique replace-

Rebreathers demand diligence and dedication to pre-dive procedures with unwavering commitment to strict safety procedures. Photo: Jill Heinerth

able batteries. You will also regularly use carbon dioxide absorbent in the form of either granular sorb or pre-packed canisters. Are these easily available in your region and the places you want to travel? You will also need to periodically change out oxygen sensors. Can you get fresh sensors locally? Sensors have a shelf life whether they are in service or not, and if you can get them locally it might save you from throwing away unused sensors that you purchased, but never installed because they are past their expiration date.

New or Used— Can you consider a used rebreather? If you find a great deal, you should budget on sending the unit back to the manufacturer to restore it to factory specifications and performance. You'll also want to start with fresh sensors. This can easily add up to several hundred if not over a thousand dollars. Be sure the deal is still worth it.

Weight and Size— Will this unit be manageable or is it too heavy to carry or too bulky to easily grasp and move?

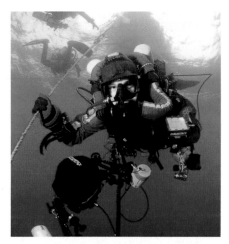

Rebreather Instructor Dr. Mel Clark hangs on a descent line in the Dominican Republic. She finds photography even more exciting and productive with the use of a rebreather. Photo: Jill Heinerth

It's a tough purchase decision and nearly everyone you ask for an opinion will have a strong one. They just bought the equivalent of a Harley-Davidson Sportster motorcycle, and will likely ooze with confidence about their buying decision. You have to be pragmatic and analytical. A try-dive experience will only help you fall in love with a harness. A comparison of cosmetics will only help you decide whether you look cool. Take time to compare features and research the unit on your own before jumping into one of the biggest purchase decisions of your underwater life.

Risk Assessment— So, how do you know if you are the right kind of diver and if you are capable of offering the proper amount of respect to the technology?

Each training agency and manufacturer has crafted a list of prerequisites for safe rebreather diving. They'll suggest that you have a nitrox qualification and can display good buoyancy control. They'll suggest that you review basic physics and be comfortable calculating partial pressures. They'll require a number of prerequisite dives. However, if you want to be a rebreather diver, you just can't tick off "been there, done that" boxes. You have to look much harder at your attitude and behavior. You must be meticulous. You must be prepared to follow strict protocols and continue using those safety protocols every time you dive, in every condition, every day, without question. You have to promise that you will never dive your rebreather if something is not functioning perfectly. You have to promise your wife, husband, kids, friends and any higher power you believe in. If you can do this, then you might be a good candidate for diving a rebreather. If you can't be diligent and disciplined, you stand a reasonable chance of dying on one.

Jill's Opinions

Now that you know a little bit about rebreathers, it is time to ask yourself if rebreather diving is right for you. If you want to make the most informed decision, you should seek further information. I have written a comprehensive book called *The Basics of Rebreather Diving* that reviews all the topics pertaining to rebreather diving and selecting the unit that is right for you. I have lost a lot of friends because of accidents they had on rebreathers. Those losses have left me saddened and forever changed. This is an enormous decision for you, your family and your heirs. If you choose to take on more risk in your diving, you better have all the facts. Rebreather diving can be extremely gratifying, but you have to accept those rewards with increased risk. I have had a wonderful career using rebreathers as a tool for ex-

*The author in her Sentinel rebreather.
Photo: Jill Heinerth*

ploration but want anyone considering them to make a careful and informed decision.

The issues that I have seen women face are usually related to fit. Some rebreathers are monsters. Counterlungs need to fit your lung size and over the shoulder counterlungs may be too bulky for women. With narrow shoulders, we simply don't have the space. Counterlungs of any type should be fitted as close to the centroid of your lungs as possible. Harnesses generally need significant modification to fit women, though fortunately many harnesses can be swapped for your meticulously adjusted technical diving harness.

I dive a Hollis Explorer, PRISM2 and a Sentinel rebreather these days, though I have owned and taught on numerous additional models. I find the light weight and adjustability of the PRISM2 to be excellent for many women, but the Explorer has me more excited than almost any new gear I have dived in the last decade. I think this unit will open a whole new world to recreational divers. It is the weight of a single tank and is very simple to operate. With backmounted lungs, it fits almost any woman without feeling bulky. It is highly capable with a two-hour range in 130 feet of water.

Reneé's Opinions

I've owned two rebreathers and both of them I'm certified to teach. I sold the Drager Dolphin SCR because it became outdated and parts were difficult to find. My PRISM Topaz CCR was sold because I lacked confidence on the unit and wasn't diving it much. I had gotten into another hobby and I had lost my skills and currency. The counterlungs were also far too big for me and I was having to make my own complicated modifications just to get the thing to fit. It breathed like a dream, but I was completely uncomfortable diving it. Someday I may have another, but not until I find one that's exactly right for me.

Women Mentors

Barbara Wynns, Mermaid

On December 15th, 2013 at age 64, Barbara Wynns swam in her last performance as a mermaid at Weeki Wachee Springs, 50 years after her dream to be a mermaid was born. She performed to honor her late husband Bobby, who was instrumental in supporting the "Mermaids of Yesteryear."

"I grew up in Florida and swam in the beautiful crystal springs all of my life. I swam in Alexander Springs, Juniper Springs, Silver Glenn Springs, Salt Springs, Rock Springs, Crystal River Springs and other northern springs. When I was 13, I visited Weeki Wachee in the summer of 1963. I saw the underwater mermaid show and I decided right then that that is what I wanted to be - a Weeki Wachee Mermaid."

Tourists have been crowding the gates of Weeki Wachee Springs since 1947 when Newt Perry opened his amazing show. The former Navy Frogman was conducting research on "hose breathing" when he came up with the idea of creating an underwater theater. From that point forward, the sleepy rural area of Weeki Wachee became known as the City of Mermaids.

In addition to the standard show featuring the "Little Mermaid," a group of veterans also performed occasional shows in the cooling waters. Some have been swimming since the park first opened. But in 1967, the City of Mermaids had a dormitory and supervising matron for the girls who lived on site. They were paid a meager wage and were responsible for all of the duties at the park including ticket sales and running the food concession. The nearest town was a great distance from Weeki Wachee which was quietly nestled in the woods. All the girls were single then, and they shared a sisterhood that endures today.

Wynns wanted to share her passion for being a mermaid and launched a very successful mermaid camp at the springs. Women from all over the country came to live their wildest dreams, learning to free dive and swim in a tail and in the process be inspired by Wynns' enthusiasm. The motivational camp was a life changing experience. Women were transformed, leaving more confident and empowered to seek and achieve new life goals. While most women bemoan their aging bodies, Barbara prepared them to rejoice in their womanhood.

"I don't believe you have to have a tail to be a mermaid. I personally believe that man, woman, tail, no tail, wetsuit, drysuit, bathing suit or no suit - if they are comfortable underwater then they are mermaids. All "merspirits" bring the underwater world to land spirits." She also feels that SCUBA diving brings a special peace to women that men may not feel. "In my experience, I sometimes see men using SCUBA as a relaxing sport. Where as with women, there is more of a spiritual bonding with their passion for being in the water."

Barbara's Aunt Dori Hale expressed it best on the occasion of her fiftieth birthday, "Barbara was a human child, as pretty as can be. There was no other in the world, that long as much as she. To leave this world of walking folks, that struggle just to dance. To swim the oceans and the springs, for this she took a chance. At seventeen, with youthful grace, and long silken tresses, she grew a tail with silver scales, and gave up all her dresses. Now thirty-two years have

passed and she's still underwater. Could it be, she'll always be the ocean's loving daughter? When those tresses are snow white and breasts and scales are sagging. Her Mother and I will always be, watching her and bragging."

Though Barbara swam her last official show at Weeki Wachee Springs State Park, she continues to use her experiences as a mermaid to motivate people and to spread messages about conserving our water planet. She is still soaking wet, often swimming and diving with her partner and treasured merman, Allen Sherrod.

Fitness and Unique Women's Health Issues

Men and women are different no doubt. Some men might tell you they won the "conceptual coin toss" when it comes gender differences. As women, we do have certain challenges that we face relatively early in development. And, at any age a woman with medical issues will have questions that revolve around her participation in recreational activities. In this chapter we will address some of the medical concerns that women may encounter and how they relate to diving. Be mindful that this is not exhaustive. Please confer with your physician and healthcare team to address your concerns more specifically.

Suunto staff diving together in France. Photo: Jill Heinerth

Gender And Diving Risk

Although we are clearly different physically the research says these differences seldom affect the sport diving experience.[4] Women appear to be equally likely to be in a diving accident as men; yet interestingly, less likely to die. According to researchers, men and women are equal when it comes to risk for decompression sickness (DCS), arterial gas embolism (AGE), venous gas embolism (VGE), oxygen toxicity and nitrogen narcosis.[4]

As women, we need to take responsibility for ourselves. It is very easy to be persuaded by others to embark on a dive that is too strenuous for us or too far beyond our skill set,

Veteran boat captain and instructor Joanna Mikutowicz prepares a dive briefing for visitors to Divetech Grand Cayman. Photo: Jill Heinerth

abilities and training. There has been a pattern established regarding dual diving deaths involving the woman diver being more novice than the male diver.[5] Do not let yourself be coerced into doing anything beyond your comfort level. The "Golden Rule" of cave diving can always be applied to any dive. "Any diver can call any dive for any reason without fear of recrimination from her buddy." Live to dive another day.

---

[4] Maida Beth Taylor, MD, MPH, FACOG, "Women and Diving: Medical and Health Considerations" in "Women and Pressure", ed. Caroline E. Fife, MD and Marguerite St. Leger Dowse, Plymouth, England, Best Publishing Company, 2010), p 103.

[5] Maida Beth Taylor, MD, MPH, FACOG, "Women and Diving: Medical and Health Considerations" in "Women and Pressure", ed. Caroline E. Fife, MD and Marguerite St. Leger Dowse, Plymouth, England, Best Publishing Company, 2010), p 104.

Diving Fitness

Fitness is defined in the American Heritage Stedman's Medical Dictionary as, "The state or condition of being physically sound and healthy especially as the result of exercise and proper nutrition; A state of general mental and physical well-being; The state of being suitably adapted to an environment."[6]

Resort Instructors like Kara from Divetech understand the importance of keeping fit for a demanding job. Photo: Jill Heinerth

Diving fitness requires that we be ready for sudden bursts of respiratory and cardiovascular efforts. Situations can arise out of nowhere that need our immediate attention. We should always be ready to respond with efficiency to any problem or emergency with ourselves and our buddy. A question to ask yourself is, "Can I, at any point during this dive, assist myself or my buddy to the surface or safe exit?" If the answer is no, perhaps it's time to re-evaluate your fitness level or modify your safe diving parameters. Think about the effort it takes to climb up a boat ladder in calm seas let alone choppy seas. If you're a cave diver, consider the exertion demanded with heavy equipment and high flow. SCUBA diving presents an inherent amount of risk for a diver, the buddy and the potential rescuer. So, your decisions about your fitness affect more than just you! Choose wisely.

If you are fit, it is a sign that you live a healthy lifestyle. Simply put, you are getting regular exercise and eating well. There are countless resources on the Internet for dietary advice and you can consult with your personal doctor. It is probably safe to say that eating fast food is not good for any of us. Even the salads and "healthy" choices at fast food restaurants can be questionable. Be mindful nutritionally. Do your research on healthy eating choices and quantities.

Exercise is available everywhere and it doesn't have to cost a dime. Get creative! Walk or ride your bicycle wherever you can. When you're at work walk the stairs, around the building and everywhere possible. Remember to eat enough to be able to complete your workouts and dive, but not enough to put on fat. Sitting is an evil monster that tries to rob you of fitness. "Researchers have linked sitting for long periods of time with a number of health concerns, including obesity," increased blood pressure, high blood sugar, increased belly fat and unhealthy cholesterol levels.[7]

---

[6] dictionary.com, "fitness," in The American Heritage® Stedman's Medical Dictionary, Houghton Mifflin Company. http://dictionary.reference.com/browse/fitness.

[7] "What are the risks of sitting too much?", Healthy Lifestyle Adult Health, http://www.mayoclinic.org/healthy-living/adult-health/expert-answers/sitting/faq-20058005.

Anatomical differences in men's and women's proportions mean that equipment and training techniques should be designed to address these dissimilarities. Photo: Jill Heinerth

Men and women divers have a lot of commonalities, however, there are physiological and anatomical differences between men and women that contribute to differential hazards and risks.[8] It might be obvious that the female skeleton generally has smaller bones than a male's. Our rib cage is smaller and it encapsulates a smaller lung mass. Our pelvis is wider and our spines have a greater lordotic (inward curvature) curve. Our legs are angled differently and are proportionally shorter than men's. We are prone to certain orthopedic injuries due to the very nature of our bone structure. Neck injuries are also more common in women. Our cranial (head) size doesn't differ much from men but our supporting structures are smaller. So we don't handle sudden acceleration or deceleration very well. Take care when doing a giant stride entry from a high entry area to protect your neck.[9] Typically, the peak performance threshold is lower for women than men. This means that we have a lower potential for power, speed, work capacity, and stamina than men. Women generally carry more fat mass than men which strains our performance. A study conducted by Pendergast et. al.[10] evaluated women divers using different types of fins. They resolved that oxygen consumption was not determined by the type of fin. Also established was that women tend to prefer a more flexible fin. Interestingly, women use 14-18% less energy regardless of the fin type or speed. The study also suggested that anatomical differences prevent women from executing deep vertical kicks "especially when using long rigid fins, and so women compensate by kicking less deeply" or rotating the fin to reduce drag.

This means that when conditions require more effort, such as strong current, women will need to kick more often, which increases the demand for energy and that decreases overall swimming efficiency. Predictably, when conditions are maxed out, our lower maximum aerobic capacity will lead to earlier exhaustion than males all being exposed to the same exertion demands.[11] Make sure your male instructor and buddy is aware of this because expecting the same results isn't sensible.

---

[8] Maida Beth Taylor, MD, MPH, FACOG, "Women and Diving: Medical and Health Considerations" in "Women and Pressure", ed. Caroline E. Fife, MD and Marguerite St. Leger Dowse, Plymouth, England, Best Publishing Company, 2010), p 97.

[9] Maida Beth Taylor, MD, MPH,FACOG, "Women and Diving: Medical and Health Considerations" in "Women and Pressure", ed. Caroline E. Fife, MD and Marguerite St. Leger Dowse (Plymouth, England: Best Publishing Company, 2010), p 98.

[10] Pendergast DR, Mollendorf J, Logue C et al. Underwater fin swimming in women with reference to fin selection. UHM 2003; 1: 75-85.

[11] [Maida Beth Taylor, MD, MPH,FACOG, "Women and Diving: Medical and Health Considerations" in "Women and Pressure", ed. Caroline E. Fife, MD and Marguerite St. Leger Dowse (Plymouth, England: Best Publishing Company, 2010), p 99

All this is to say that we need to do all we can in our power to obtain and maintain fitness. Ten recognized general physical skills are stamina, strength, flexibility, power, cardiovascular/respiratory endurance, coordination, balance, agility and accuracy. If you are competent in each of these skills then you are considered fit. Find training or exercise where you can practice these. You can do this by maintaining variety in your workouts. Bicycling, rowing, running, swimming, and CrossFit are great ways to get variety and have fun. Be able to perform endurance activities, sprinting activities and everything in between.[12] We want to be able to respond to very unpredictable situations quickly, so avoiding the same exercise regime will be most effective. Get regular, possibly annual, checkups with your physician to evaluate you for any developing conditions, diseases or general health issues especially as you age.

If you are taking a SCUBA class of any kind you will likely be asked to fill out the Recreational SCUBA Training Council (RSTC) Medical Form. This form includes a questionnaire for students. If you answer affirmatively to any of the questions, you will be asked to visit with your doctor to evaluate your fitness to dive. This form includes four pages of notes for your physician. You should take those with you to your appointment. Few general practitioners have had much or any experience with diving medicine and may need to refer you to someone with more knowledge. When prescription medications are involved, it may be more difficult for them to evaluate your fitness to dive and they may need to consult some of the references cited on that form.

Medication While Diving

A general rule of thumb regarding medication is to not dive with it in your system until you've tried it with success on land first. Medications can have side effects like dizziness, drowsiness or decreased alertness and these effects can be multiplied at depth. Some of these side effects may also predispose you to other issues such as oxygen toxicity, inert gas narcosis or decompression sickness. If you experience undesirable side effects while diving on medication either stop diving or stop the medication. Some prescription medications must not be stopped without a physician's endorsement.

Research the medications you are taking to find out if they are suitable to take while diving. Malaria prevention medication can be a little tough on the system. Doxycycline

---

[12] "What Is Fitness?", The CrossFit Journal, accessed April 1, 2014, http://library.crossfit.com/free/pdf/CFJ-trial.pdf

has been personally experienced by one of the authors to cause extreme nausea with exertion underwater.

Read, understand and be alert for the possible side effects of using a medication and discuss these with your doctor in the context of diving. Reliable information is available at www.diversalertnetwork.org. DAN's non-emergency phone line is also available to members who have medical questions. A doctor will answer your questions about specific medications or physical conditions or will refer you to another DAN physician who will call you back with pertinent information.

Proper Hydration

It is rather ironic that the beloved sport that immerses us in water causes us to lose it. We've all experienced it. Just before the dive we go pee to prevent the urge during the dive. And you guessed it....it happens anyway! You can thank your hypothalamus. The hypothalamus is a section of the brain responsible for hormone production. It is small but still controls many required functions of the body. The primary function of the hypothalamus is homeostasis, which is a system-wide status quo in the body.[13] Like a rebreather, the hypothalamus uses a setpoint to regulate the body's systems. The setpoint stays fixed, but the hypothalamus determines a deviation limit where it

Rather than relying on bottled water for hydration, think ahead and use a refillable flask or bottle. You'll be doing something good for yourself and the planet at the same time.

will initiate compensatory changes. As divers, there are things we do that cause this deviation. Anytime we submerge ourselves in water, especially cooler water, our blood begins to shunt or travel from the extremities and skin to the chest to warm and protect critical areas. This causes an increase in core blood volume although the total volume does not change. The hypothalamus mistakes this as fluid overload and tells the kidneys to produce urine. Suddenly we have the urge to pee....and pee....and pee during the dive. This reflex is referred to as immersion diuresis. When climbing back on board the boat or up the beach in a freshwater lake, the blood flows back to the legs. A drop in blood pressure occurs and you might feel a little lightheaded until everything gets in balance again. There is nothing we can do to prevent immersion diuresis. After the dive is over, begin hydrating as soon as possible to regain homeostasis. You'll probably feel the urge to pee again shortly after surfacing.

Believe it or not, men and women generally have roughly the same size bladders holding up to about 19.9 ounces/500ml of fluid. The bladder wall has receptors that can tell when it is being stretched. These receptors signal the brain when it is time to start think-

---

[13] "Hypothalamus," Healthline Body Maps, www.healthline.com/human-body-maps/hypothalamus.

ing about voiding, which is at about half full. What may be different for all of us is the frequency of urination and that has a direct effect on the size of the bladder. If you void often your bladder may not be comfortable holding the average amount of urine.[14]

Well what, you might ask, does that have to do with diving? Most divers probably consider hydration prior to diving more than any other time. Scientists have shown that dehydration is present in most cases of decompression illness and therefore we assume that proper hydration may reduce our likelihood of getting bent. We can't prove that dehydration leads to increased DCI risk, but most will agree that good hydration is important for general wellness. But, let's dig a little deeper. Hydration should begin well before the dive. Our bodies only process a little water at a time so chugging a gallon right before the dive isn't really helping. Ensure proper hydration days, maybe even a week before diving activities. In fact, it's a good idea to stay hydrated all the time. So after your dives, keep drinking water. If you're on a dive trip, you should constantly hydrate. Hydration isn't just about drinking water. It's all about fluid balance. Sweating, salt water, certain beverages and foods and exercise can all lead to dehydration. Drink hydrating fluids like water, non-alcoholic, low-sugar and caffeine-free beverages. Single serve Crystal Light or performance electrolyte-laden beverage packets, for example, are great to add to your water bottle. Consider purchasing a reusable, collapsible water bottle. They are convenient and are environmentally more responsible than plastic disposable water bottles.

Post dive socializing is fun for sure. But, do not dive with a hangover! Your body is compromised after a night of drinking alcoholic beverages. This is not only miserable it is dangerous. Don't drink and dive!

What keeps us from hydrating? Some divers actually don't drink enough fluids because they are afraid they'll have to urinate while underwater. If the boat doesn't have a toilet and you don't want to pee in your exposure suit, there's a problem. Don't intentionally dehydrate yourself.

There's an age old saying that there are two kinds of divers. There are those who pee in their wetsuit and those who lie about it. Speaking to the people who admit to it, hydration is key. Proper hydration dilutes the urine making it nearly colorless and odorless. If your pee is not clear or very pale (unless you're taking certain vitamins or supplements) then you're not hydrated enough. You can pee in your wetsuit and avoid embarrassment simply by being well hydrated. Immersion diuresis will probably happen anyway so set yourself up for success. If you think that by peeing in your wetsuit you are staying warmer think again. You will be warmer for a bit as the vessels at the skin's surface dilate and transfer heat. Once the cooler water enters the suit the vessels constrict reducing thermal conductivity and now you are colder than you were before!

---

[14] "Is A Man's Bladder Larger or Smaller Than That of a Woman?", The Body Beautiful, www.theguardian.com/notesandqueries/0,,01820,00.html.

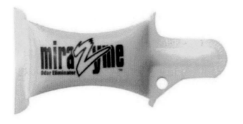

Wetsuit deodorizers such as Sink the Stink and Mirazyme can be carried on trips in small single use containers.

As women, we also want to protect our skin. Urine is sterile and safe. It isn't harmful to your skin unless you leave it there for a while when a rash could possibly develop. Give your wetsuit a good freshwater flush when the dive is over to rinse your skin and the suit. Occasionally shampoo and deodorize your exposure suits. McNett and "Sink The Stink" products offer excellent cleaning and deodorizing products for your exposure suit to help keep them from reeking.

If there are no proper facilities for relieving yourself, you might consider using specifically designed appliances that make urination discreet. Manufacturers have built unique female urination devices that assist with convenience and privacy. The "Go Girl" and other similar devices are designed for topside use. They consist of a soft rubber, silicone or plastic funnel that is angled in such a way that the cup can be placed over the urethra and the urine will flow out of the lower end of the funnel and over the side of a boat or into a toilet bowl that you would rather not sit on. You can comfortably pee standing up. The "She-P" and the "Shewee" can be utilized topside or underwater through a specially designed outlet valve placed in your drysuit. These are described in the equipment section of the book.

Go Girl and SheWee devices are convenient for voiding discreetly or for use in less-than-sanitary bathrooms and heads where you don't want to sit down.

Production of urine is one of the body's responses to cold so layer up. Products such as Sharkskin and Lavacore are excellent to wear alone or under your wetsuit for added warmth without adding buoyancy. After your dive, bundle up if you are cold and stay out of the wind. Get your wetsuit off and get dry.

Thermal Issues

Staying warm is not only for your comfort but for your survival. Thermal tolerance has a lot to do with a woman's percentage of body fat and her ratio of surface area to body mass. Fat has low thermal conductivity so it acts as insulation. "Lean women (less than 27% body fat) have a large surface area to body mass ratio and therefore cool at a faster rate" than men. If she has more than 30% body fat she will "maintain similar low levels of heat production when placed in cool water" as a man.[15] It does seem though that women have less tolerance to cold than men do. If you find that you are sensitive to cold while diving, you can take preventative measures. Underwater we lose heat much more quickly than on land. A trick is to not let yourself get cold before the dive begins. If the weather is

---

[15] dspace.rubicon-foundation.org/xmlui/bitstream/handle/123456789/6212/SPUMS_V8N3_28.PDF?sequence=1

cooler stay layered up being sure to wear a warm hat and scarf or neck gaiter. Merino wool and technical materials such as Thinsulate, Capilene and Polartec are engineered for warmth. Cotton garments will stay damp and cool. A hood will conserve warmth and keep your mask strap from pulling your hair. Choose the appropriate thermal protection for the water temperature and planned dive duration. The water may be 85°F/29°C; but after several dives, you may get chilly on a night dive. If you're diving in water that has thermo-clines, such as a freshwater lake, dress for the temperatures at maximum depth. It will be much colder at 100 feet/30 meters than it is at 20 feet/6 meters especially in the summertime when the air temperatures are hot.

Merino wool is nature's ideal base layer. It is excellent at regulating body temperature when worn against the skin, helping to draw sweat away from the skin through wicking. Photo: Courtesy of Santi Diving

Some over-the-counter prescription drugs can interfere with your body's mechanisms for con-serving heat, typically by preventing the constric-tion of blood vessels near the skin. Antihistamines do this. Alcohol is worse. Check labels and ask your doctor if anything you are taking might be rob-bing you of heat.

Staying warm may be an issue for most, but for others, heat sensitivity is a great men-ace. In some parts of the world, water temperatures can get quite warm. If you wear ex-cessive exposure protection you can easily overheat. "The female's body temperature will rise 2-3 degrees higher than the male's before the cooling process of sweating begins. Also the female has fewer functional sweat glands."[16] If it is excessively hot outside, do things to stay cool like get out of the sun, dress in lighter colors and try to reduce or at least budget your exertion to keep from overheating. Conditions permitting, take a dunk in the water to cool off or use the boat's shower to lower your temperature. Everyone is different and has varying tolerances to cold and heat. Know your body and plan ac-cordingly. No matter the air and water tempera-tures, stay thermally protected and hydrated.

When planning for a trip, think about the dif-ferent types of thermal protection you might need. If you are exiting a Zodiac on a beach and want to stay dry, you might need rubber boots. If you are assisting divers from a boat, you might need waterproof gloves. A warm hat on any day is almost essential after a dive. Photo: Courtesy of www.SednaEpic.-com - Jill Heinerth

---

[16] dspace.rubicon-foundation.org/xmlui/bitstream/handle/123456789/6212/SPUMS_V8N3_28.PDF?sequence=1

Careers in Diving

Maida Taylor MD, MPH, FACOG

Dr. Maida Taylor received a Bachelor of Science in biology and Russian from Tufts University, a Masters of Public Health from University of California in Berkeley, and her M.D. from Stanford University Medical School. Dr. Taylor opened a solo private practice office in San Francisco where she had an active practice until 2001. She has also served at Lilly Pharmaceuticals, Novo Nordisk, Inc. and Esprit Pharma.

Dr. Taylor's areas of special interest and expertise include drugs for incontinence, mood disorders and osteoporosis, breast cancer risk reduction, the female athletic triad (interaction of disordered eating, amenorrhea, and osteoporosis), cancer epidemiology, breast cancer risk reduction strategies, pediatric gynecology, geriatric gynecology, and gynecologic care for the developmentally disabled. She also studies the interactions and influences of hormones, menstruation, menopause and pregnancy on fitness, and the effects of hormonal changes in diving performance. Her current area of concern is the effects of low estrogen states on the incidence and severity of decompression illness.

Dr. Taylor has been diving since 1975. Her contribution to the diving world has been primarily through writing, research, and education. She authored a chapter, "Women in Diving" in the first and all subsequent editions of Bove and Davis's *Textbook of Diving Medicine.* She also authored the chapter on medical and health considerations of women and diving in Fife and St Leger Dowse's *Women and Pressure,* which chronicles achievements of pioneering women in diving, altitude and space environments.

Dr. Taylor admits to having and overcoming claustrophobia. This, coupled with fear of being trapped in an overhead environment have been her greatest challenges as a woman diver.

As a small woman, Dr. Taylor has encountered and resolved equipment challenges with her BCD and fins. Her advice to other women divers is, "Know your limits and don't be afraid to express them." Dr. Taylor's experience has taught her that the water to sur-face transition can be both challenging and strenuous. If a diver was considering to dive or not based on surface conditions, she would counsel others saying, "know what you can and can't do before you're there and don't give in to peer pressure. Ask yourself, Do I feel like diving today? If the answer is no, then don't!"

Dr. Taylor is a down to earth woman highly accomplished in writing, diving medical research and education. With all of her vast experience and knowledge Maida believes that her greatest reward as a diver was the day she met her husband.

The authors are incredibly grateful for Dr. Taylor's guidance and support in creating this book. Her body of work has furthered the sport of diving for women and inspired many of us to recognize that there are truly few barriers to us based on our physiology.

Gynecological Concerns

Premenstrual Syndrome (PMS)

DAN describes PMS as "a group of psychophysiological symptoms that are poorly defined with a deficiency in understanding that occur during the latter part of the menstrual cycle."[17] For many of us PMS could include symptoms including depression, angry outbursts, irritability, anxiety, confusion, social withdrawal, breast tenderness, abdominal bloating, headache or swelling of the extremities. About 80% of all women experience symptoms of PMS; but, a diagnosis of PMS requires at least one of the symptoms be present during the five days prior to menses (period) in three prior menstrual cycles.[18]

Reneé Power glides over the Kittiwake. Photo: Jill Heinerth

Premenstrual Dysphoric Disorder (PMDD) affects 5% of women and is a more severe form of PMS. These women may be disrupted socially and professionally. Care should be taken to properly diagnose that the woman has PMDD and not some other underlying and concurrent psychiatric or physical disease.[19] PMDD can exacerbate underlying emotional disorders and is more disruptive than PMS. To be diagnosed with PMDD a woman must have five of the above listed symptoms and experience "decreased interest in activities, difficulty concentrating, lack of energy, changes in appetite, change in sleep pattern, and feelings of being overwhelmed or out of control." This disorder leads to great social disruption because of the intensity of the symptoms produced.

According to DAN, "research has shown that accidents in general are more common among women during PMS. If women suffer from premenstrual syndrome it may be wise to dive conservatively during this time. There is no scientific evidence, however that they are more susceptible to decompression illness or dive injuries/accidents."[20] If a woman during PMS finds herself experiencing depression or feeling antisocial, she should evalu-

---

[17] DAN Medical Frequently Asked Questions, www.diversalertnetwork.org/medical/faq/Premenstrual_Syndrome.

[18] Maida Beth Taylor, MD, MPH,FACOG, "Women and Diving: Medical and Health Considerations" in "Women and Pressure", ed. Caroline E. Fife, MD and Marguerite St. Leger Dowse (Plymouth, England: Best Publishing Company, 2010), p 123.

[19] Maida Beth Taylor, MD, MPH,FACOG, "Women and Diving: Medical and Health Considerations" in "Women and Pressure", ed. Caroline E. Fife, MD and Marguerite St. Leger Dowse (Plymouth, England: Best Publishing Company, 2010), p 124.

[20] DAN Medical Frequently Asked Questions, www.diversalertnetwork.org/medical/faq/Premenstrual_Syndrome).

Diving icon Dr. Sylvia Earle, born in 1935, remains an active diver and tireless conservationist, focusing her efforts on developing a global network of land and ocean areas that can safeguard the living systems of our planet. These efforts hope to stabilize and promote resiliency in response to rapidly accelerating climate change. She will not allow her age slow her down in her pursuits. Photo: Cis Lunar Development Labs

ate her fitness to dive. The risk is present not only for her but for her buddy.[21] Dr. Maida Beth Taylor recommends that some women with PMS or PMDD should be evaluated for fitness to dive to be sure she doesn't have some other pervasive mood disorder. She states strongly that anyone, whether male or female, who displays destructive behavior, suicidal or antisocial tendencies or other severe psychiatric disturbances, should be disqualified from diving.

Menopause

Many heath issues blamed on menopause are simply due to aging. Menopause is not the greatest risk factor for women divers, it is age related diseases that go undiagnosed such as diabetes, hypertension and coronary artery disease.[22] If a woman diver is suspected to have DCI, physicians should consider potential stroke related to the use of hormone therapy while evaluating the neurological symptoms. If a woman diver is over 60 years of age, the risk of stroke dramatically increases. Hormone therapy enhances propagation of intravascular thrombus formation (blood clot) increasing the potential severity of a DCI event.

Endometriosis

Endometriosis is "a disease in which tissue similar to the lining inside the uterus (called the endometrium), is found outside the uterus, where it induces a chronic inflammatory reaction that may result in scar tissue. It is primarily found on the pelvic peritoneum, ovaries, in the recto-vaginal septum, on the bladder and bowel."[23] Symptoms include increased bleeding, cramping and increase in the amount/duration of menstrual flow. When experiencing severe symptoms you may not want to dive. The pain from endometriosis may be so severe that you have trouble getting through your daily activities and it may be in your best interest to suspend diving until symptoms have subsided. According to DAN

---

[21] DAN Medical Frequently Asked Questions, www.diversalertnetwork.org/medical/faq/Premenstrual_Syndrome).

[22] Maida Beth Taylor, MD, MPH,FACOG, "Women and Diving: Medical and Health Considerations" in "Women and Pressure", ed. Caroline E. Fife, MD and Marguerite St. Leger Dowse (Plymouth, England: Best Publishing Company, 2010), p 123.

[23] "Endometriosis," DAN Medical Frequently Asked Questions, www.diversalertnetwork.org/medical/faq/Endometriosis

there is "no evidence that a woman with endometriosis diving at other times is at any greater risk of diving-related disease than a person without this condition." [24]

Ovarian cancer

Ovarian tumors can be cancerous (malignant) or non-cancerous (benign) and are fairly common. Sadly, there is currently no reliable screening. The main issue for diving is recovery from surgery and chemotherapy side effects. As mentioned earlier, some chemotherapy drugs "can cause pulmonary toxicity and patients can have residual pulmonary functional impairment for a year or longer after they have finished treatment."[25]

Hysterectomy/Salpingo-Oophorectomy

A hysterectomy is a surgical procedure where the uterus is removed through the abdomen or through the vagina. A salpingo-oophorectomy is a surgical procedure where the Fallopian tubes and ovaries are removed. Both of these operations

After any surgery, it might be a while before you are able to lift and carry heavy equipment. If your doctor approves your return to diving, you can use good strategies to carry your gear. You can don your equipment in the water and ask for help getting it back onto a boat. Photo: Courtesy of Aqualung

are considered major surgery and the same rules apply as breast surgery (discussed later) regarding recovery and healing prior to diving. The healing time is usually 6-8 weeks or longer provided there were no complications. Before you resume diving or carry heavy diving equipment be sure to get medical clearance from your doctor.

Birth Control

The side effects of using oral contraceptives may include dizziness, nausea, headaches and fluid retention. "Oral contraceptives may also be associated with an increase in blood pressure and an increased risk of thromboembolic disorders (development of clot-like vein occlusions, which can lead to an emboli)." [26]

---

[24] "DAN Explores Fitness and Diving Issues for Women," www.diversalertnetwork.org, Donna M. Uguccioni, M.S., DAN Associate Medical Director Dr. Richard Moon, and Dr. Maida Beth Taylor

[25] "DAN Explores Fitness and Diving Issues for Women," www.diversalertnetwork.org/medical/articles/DAN_-Explores_Fitness_and_Diving_Issues_for_Women,. Donna M. Uguccioni, M.S., DAN Associate Medical Director Dr. Richard Moon, and Dr. Maida Beth Taylor

[26] "Oral Birth Control," DAN Medical Frequently Asked Questions, www.diversalertnetwork.org/medical/faq/Oral_Birth_Control

Due to hormonal changes, women on oral contraceptives may be more susceptible due to increased water retention and reduction in venous tone (property of the venous system, reflecting the venous resistance and pressure inside the veins). In theory, scientists feel that this could cause the blood to sludge and reduce elimination of nitrogen, but there are currently no data to support this. Hopefully future research will indicate whether they may increase an individual's susceptibility to decompression illness or other diving disorders. To date, there is no indication to substantiate that use of oral contraceptives in recreational diving is a contraindication. If oral contraceptives are a clinical problem for you on the surface, the problems could be magnified on a dive. If unsure contact Divers Alert Network for advice regarding medications and diving.

Some women have underlying coagulation (blood clotting) defects that could contribute to DCS. If you or another female encounter an "undeserved hit" that doesn't make sense based on the dive profile, contributing factors, dive log and history think about oral contraceptive use.[27]

Intrauterine Contraceptive Devices (IUDs)

Although IUDs pose no additional hazard for the female diver, amount and duration of menstrual flow is generally increased. This may be inconvenient if you are diving in a remote area or if there are no facilities or privacy.[28]

The Mirena Intrauterine system, is a steroid-embedded contraceptive device that seeks to address the problem above. It is designed to deliver very high local levels of progestin levonorgestrel directly to the endometrium. This type of device can greatly reduce the amount of flow a woman experiences during her cycle. To a woman diver this may have inviting benefits if she endures heavy bleeding.[29]

Barriers and Spermicides

Some women who use these methods for birth control question whether the agents may become ineffective due to immersion and dilution if water washes in and out of the vagina. Although no failure rates have ever been documented for female divers who use diaphragms, foams, creams, caps, jellies and films, the efficacy may be reduced due to dilution of the concentration of the active contraceptive chemical agent present with these barrier methods. With a drysuit this isn't an issue. If you use a wetsuit the amount of flushing is probably minimal, however there are no guarantees as to the effectiveness of

---

[27] "Oral Birth Control," DAN Medical Frequently Asked Questions, www.diversalertnetwork.org/medical/faq/Oral_Birth_Control

[28] "DAN Explores Fitness and Diving Issues for Women," www.diversalertnetwork.org/medical/articles/DAN_Explores_Fitness_and_Diving_Issues_for_Women, Donna M. Uguccioni, M.S., DAN Associate Medical Director Dr. Richard Moon, and Dr. Maida Beth Taylor

[29] Bove and Davis' Diving Medicine 4th Edition; Women in Diving, Maida Beth Taylor, chapter 19, p. 399.

these methods after diving.[30] There are currently no known hazards to female divers associated with barrier methods of contraception.[31]

Ortho Evra Patch

Ortho Evra is a relatively new, very popular contraceptive option. It is a transdermal contraceptive patch releasing both morelgestromin and ethinyl estradiol into the bloodstream every 24 hours. The patch is safe to use while swimming and exercising and adheres well. The product literature says that if the patch comes off, then simply replace it with a new one on dry skin. Adherence of the patch with diving has not been documented.[32]

NuvaRing

NuvaRing is a flexible, colorless vaginal ring that is approximately 2.1 inches in diameter that contains the hormones etonogestrel and ethinyl estradiol. It has proven to be efficient and brings with it the same risk as other contraceptives with the same hormones. The ring is to be left in place for 21 days, then removed for 7. There is very little clinical experience regarding diving and prolonged periods of immersion and how that might affect the performance of the device.[33]

Injectable Contraceptives

There are a few long acting, injectable medoxyprogesterone acetate or medoxyprogesterone acetate plus estradiol contraceptive options available. These may be referred to as Depo-Provera and Lunelle respectively. These are becoming more popular, especially with younger women. Regarding diving, Lunelle, or equivalent contraceptives (depo contraceptives with estrogen), may offer similar thromboembolic (clotting) risks found in oral contraceptives. If a woman does experience decompression sickness (DCS) and she is taking a contraceptive with progestational agents it is highly speculated based on studies in the 1970s, that she may receive some protection from tissue damage.

Diving and Conception

According to Diver's Alert Network "there is indeed no data or available literature that addresses this specific topic." The appropriate experts DAN consulted have the opinion that since little is known if there would be any detrimental effect on conception, a woman should suspend diving activities in order to create the best possible environment for fertility. Some experts say that if a woman is diving, she should "wait 48 hours after diving be-

---

[30] "DAN Explores Fitness and Diving Issues for Women," Donna M. Uguccioni, M.S., DAN Associate Medical Director Dr. Richard Moon, and Dr. Maida Beth Taylor

[31] Bove and Davis' Diving Medicine 4th Edition; Women in Diving, Maida Beth Taylor, chapter 19, p. 399.

[32] Bove and Davis' Diving Medicine 4th Edition; Women in Diving, Maida Beth Taylor, chapter 19, p 397.

[33] Bove and Davis' Diving Medicine 4th Edition; Women in Diving, Maida Beth Taylor, chapter 19, p. 398.

fore attempting conception" to allow for proper nitrogen off-gassing.[34] For yourself, you should weigh the risk versus benefit and make an informed decision to dive or not.

Pregnancy

Diving is not without risk for anyone no matter if you are pregnant or not. There is currently little research and limited or inconsistent data available and almost no human research due to the risk and ethical challenges. The current and past trend has been for women to not dive while pregnant. There have been anecdotal reports of women diving repeatedly while pregnant without any complications. You may find comfort in this if you found that you accidentally went diving while pregnant. DAN research says, "There is certainly insufficient evidence to warrant termination of a pregnancy."[35]

After delivery, women may return to diving relatively quickly. If the delivery was via C-section, then healing may take at least six to eight weeks. Photo: Jill Heinerth

However, there are numerous ethical concerns at hand. If you know you are pregnant and you intentionally SCUBA dive you are effectively accepting risk for another person. Diving is optional and the risk to you or the child while diving pregnant is completely avoidable. Physicians have some guidance for diving and non-diving pregnant patients regarding prescribed hyperbaric therapy. They advise that "the evidence suggests that the risk to the fetus with treatment is lower than without."[36] Although it is possible to dive pregnant without complications, the risk is still there and the outcome could be devastating for all. As an adult you have to make your own decisions weighing both the risk and benefit for all involved including your child. The most prudent and conservative choice would be to not dive during a known pregnancy.

When should you dive again after giving birth? This depends on your conditioning and level of exercise pre and post delivery and if the delivery was vaginal or a Cesarean (C-Section). If the delivery was vaginal, "women can usually resume light to moderate activity within one to three weeks."[37] If you are returning to sports and exercise programs it is

---

[34] "Diving and Conception," DAN Medical Frequently Asked Questions, www.diversalertnetwork.org/medical/faq/diving-and-conception

[35] "Pregnancy," DAN Medical Frequently Asked Questions, www.diversalertnetwork.org/medical/faq/Pregnancy

[36] "Pregnancy," DAN Medical Frequently Asked Questions, www.diversalertnetwork.org/medical/faq/Pregnancy

[37] "Return To Diving After Giving Birth", DAN Medial Frequently Asked Questions, www.diversalertnetwork.org/medical/faq/Return_To_Diving_After_Giving_Birth

suggested to "wait three to four weeks after giving birth."[38] If there were pregnancy and or delivery complications the time should be extended. If the delivery was a C-section it is advised to wait "at least six to eight weeks after a C-section before returning to diving"[39] due to carrying heavy dive equipment, wound healing and lost physical conditioning. If you encountered any further complications like hypertension, diabetes, twins or triplets or pre-term labor may require a longer delay back to diving. It is always advisable to check with your physician prior to diving. Another consideration is your stamina level with a newborn. Make sure you are mentally fit and rested before resuming diving activities.[40]

Breath Health Issues

Breast Feeding

Inert gas such as nitrogen is absorbed into the mother's tissues after breathing compressed air or other gas mixtures. Inert gas is not used in metabolism. Washout occurs quickly from the tissues and fluids in the body. "Insignificant amounts of this nitrogen would be present in the mother's breast milk; there is, however, no risk of the infant accumulating this nitrogen."[41] There is currently no evidence that diving affects lactation in any way.

Breast Implants

The goals for breast implants are diversified based on the individual. Some reasons are "to have larger breasts; to balance the size or shape of uneven breasts; to make the breasts more proportional with the rest of the body; to enhance breasts that have lost volume and shape due to pregnancy, nursing, weight loss or age; and to reshape or reconstruct the breast after surgery." Women who are pregnant, nursing or who have breast cancer are ineligible for breast augmentation.[42]

Breast implants are currently available in three types- silicone filled, saline filled and silicone-saline-filled. In a study by Dr. Richard Vann, Vice President of Research at DAN, breast implants were placed in the Duke University Medical Center hyperbaric chamber. The study included testing of all three types simulating recreational SCUBA diving profiles varying the depth and time. (Note that the studies did not simulate the implant in human tissue). The results showed an "insignificant increase in bubble size (one to four percent)

38 "Return To Diving After Giving Birth", DAN Medial Frequently Asked Questions, www.diversalertnetwork.org/medical/faq/Return_To_Diving_After_Giving_Birth

39 "Return To Diving After Giving Birth", DAN Medial Frequently Asked Questions, www.diversalertnetwork.org/medical/faq/Return_To_Diving_After_Giving_Birth

40 "Return To Diving After Giving Birth", DAN Medial Frequently Asked Questions, www.diversalertnetwork.org/medical/faq/Return_To_Diving_After_Giving_Birth

41 "DAN Explores Fitness and Diving Issues for Women," www.diversalertnetwork.org/medical/articles/DAN_Explores_Fitness_and_Diving_Issues_for_Women, Donna M. Uguccioni, M.S., DAN Associate Medical Director Dr. Richard Moon, and Dr. Maida Beth Taylor

42 "Breast Augmentation Surgery," www.diversalertnetwork.org/medical/articles/Breast_Augmentation_Surgery

in both saline and silicone gel implants, depending on the depth and duration of the dive. The least volume change occurred in the saline-filled implant because nitrogen is less soluble in saline than silicone. The silicone-saline-filled type showed the greatest volume change. Bubble formation in implants led to a small volume increase, which is not likely to damage the implants or surrounding tissue. If gas bubbles do form in the implant they resolve over time."[43]

Some BCDs are equipped with an adjustable chest strap that can slide up or down. This may be extremely important for comfort for some women. Photo: Jill Heinerth

DAN recommends a medical evaluation prior to diving after surgery. You will need to be evaluated for proper healing and infection risk. Be prepared to wait the sufficient time needed for healing and comfortable diving. You may find that your SCUBA equipment fits differently after your surgery. Your exposure suit may fit more snugly than it did before and feel uncomfortable until soreness has resolved. Consider different sizing and very stretchy neoprene for comfort. Slight modifications may be needed to reduce chest constriction from your BCD chest strap. DAN suggests that constrictive BCDs may contribute to implant leaks. Saline filled implants are neutrally buoyant and the silicone filled are more negative. If your breast implants are larger, your trim may be altered significantly. Adjust your trim with creative trim weight placement and practice to get your buoyancy dialed in. You may not be able to reach things such as your dry suit exhaust valve as easily. Practice in a controlled environment such as a pool until you are comfortable again.

Breast Cancer

Breast cancer is the second leading cause of cancer death in women, exceeded only by skin cancer. "Approximately 1 in 8 (12%) women will develop breast cancer in their lifetime."[44] "The chance that breast cancer will be responsible for a woman's death is about 1 in 36 (about 3%)."[45] Fortunately the rates of death have declined since about 2000. This is thought to be because of a decrease of post menopausal hormone therapy treatment. These rates have been stable in recent years.

Lumps can be benign but breast cancer is malignant. It starts developing in the cells of the breast and these cells clump together to form the malignant tumor. These cells can also invade surrounding tissues or even distant areas of the body. The American Cancer Society's estimates for breast cancer in the United States for 2014 are:

---

[43] "Breast Implants," DAN Medical Frequently Asked Questions, www.diversalertnetwork.org/medical/faq/Breast_implants

[44] "What are the key statistics about breast cancer?" Learn About Cancer, www.cancer.org/cancer/breastcancer/detailedguide/breast-cancer-key-statistics

[45] www.cancer.org/cancer/breastcancer/detailedguide/breast-cancer-key-statistics

-About 232,670 new cases of invasive breast cancer will be diagnosed in women.

-About 62,570 new cases of carcinoma in situ (CIS) will be diagnosed (CIS is non-invasive and is the earliest form of breast cancer).

-About 40,000 women will die from breast cancer.

Early breast cancer detection is recommended by the American Cancer Society.

-Women age 40 and older should have a screening mammogram every year and should continue to do so for as long as they are in good health.

-Women in their 20s and 30s should have a clinical breast exam (CBE) as part of a periodic (regular) health exam by a health professional, at least every 2 years. After age 40, women should have a breast exam by a health professional every year.

-Breast self-exam (BSE) is an option for women starting in their 20s. Women should be told about the benefits and limitations of BSE. Women should report any breast changes to their health professional right away.

-Women at high risk for breast cancer based on certain factors should get an MRI and a mammogram every year.[46]

With regards to diving, issues with breast cancer and diving will be largely based on surgical, radiation therapy and or chemotherapy discussed later in this chapter.

Currently in the United States there are over 2.5 million breast cancer survivors! Due to medical advances this number is expected to grow. As this number rises, so will the number of diving breast cancer survivors. In 2000, over one third of all PADI certified SCUBA divers were women. SCUBA diving has been introduced to breast cancer survivors as a way to increase mental and physical wellness. Although there are a lot of support groups in the diving community for the survivors of breast cancer there is still so much we don't understand. Project Pink Tank has a goal

Rosemary Lunn sports her helmet from Light Monkey; supporting Project Pink Tank. Photo: Jill Heinerth

to understand better the mental and physical health of the diving breast cancer survivor. During this project the potential mental and physical benefits of long term cancer therapy will be researched. Data are provided by the documented survivors and analyzed by Duke Dive Medicine research personnel.[47]

---

[46] "American Cancer Society recommendations for early breast cancer detection", Learn About Cancer, www.cancer.org/cancer/breastcancer/detailedguide/breast-cancer-detection

[47] rubicon-foundation.org/Projects/project-pink-tank/

Cancer Treatment

Explore the numerous treatment options that are available to you. Treatment is a process and a progression. Get to know your care team as they will be on this journey through uncharted territory with you. They truly care and will both laugh and cry with you. You will even be thought about when you're not at the facility receiving active treatment. Much more in-depth information available by your physician or trusted and reliable Internet sites such as www.cancer.org.

Radiation Therapy

This type of therapy utilizes high energy X-rays that destroy the cancer cells. In the case of breast cancer, radiation therapy is usually applied to the breast tissue after a lumpectomy or partial mastectomy to reduce the probability that the cancer will come back in the nearby lymph nodes or the breast itself. After a full mastectomy your doctor may recommend radiation therapy depending on the size of the tumor and/or if it had spread to the lymph nodes.

Each woman who has been stricken with cancer will have her own unique issues to consider before returning to diving. Her care team will look holistically at issues as diverse as wound healing, strength and ongoing medications. Photo: Jill Heinerth

Two types of radiation are available. External beam radiation uses a big machine on the outside of the body to focus the radiation beam to a specific area on the inside. It feels like getting an X-ray and is painless; but, the radiation is far more intense. Short term side effects may include swelling in the breast, fatigue and a sunburned look to the irradiated area. These changes may resolve anywhere from 6 months to 2 years. Be aware that you may experience breast firmness changes. Your future option to have reconstructive surgery may be affected. Brachytherapy or internal radiation treats from the inside of the body. Radioactive seeds or pellets are strategically placed around the breast cancer tumor. This method can be used as a stand alone treatment or combined with external radiation therapy. Discuss all of this with your care team to help with your treatment course and decision making regarding a return to diving after treatment.

Chemotherapy

Very simply, cancer killing drugs are either injected through a vein or taken orally (by mouth) and will reach most parts of the body traveling through the bloodstream. Chemotherapy (chemo) is delivered in cycles of treatment and recovery possibly lasting several months. Some common side effects include mouth sores, hair loss, loss of appetite, decreased appetite, nausea and vomiting, low blood cell counts, increased chance of infections, easy bruising or bleeding, menstrual changes and fatigue. Chemotherapy is far more involved than discussed here. We invite you to discuss this topic further and in more detail with your cancer care team.

Radiation and chemotherapy drugs can cause pulmonary toxicity. Before diving your physician will need to evaluate you to "include an assessment of the lung to ensure that damage likely to predispose the diver to pulmonary barotrauma (arterial gas embolism, pneumothorax or pneumomediastinum) is not present." [48] Additionally, healing must have occurred. Before a doctor approves you for diving, they will evaluate whether healing has been satisfactory and whether immersion in fresh or salt water could contribute to wound infection. Infection risk may have been temporarily elevated during treatment and your immune system should have returned to normal function prior to diving.

Surgical Treatments

Most women with breast cancer (and some with benign tumors) endure some type of surgery. It may be a lumpectomy (removing the lump and a little surrounding tissue) or a quadrantectomy where one-quarter of the breast is removed. A mastectomy is a removal of the entire breast and possibly nearby tissues. This surgical procedure ranges from simple to radical depending on the amount of tissue removed.

If you have breast cancer or breast surgery for malignant or non-malignant tumors and are undergoing treatment or have had treatment consult your physician before diving. You may not feel like diving because of the symptoms of treatment. Side effects are unpleasant and energy may be low. Healing may be painful and make wearing equipment uncomfortable. Lifting gear may be out of the question for quite a while. Finally, your cognitive skills and concentration may be compromised and you might make poor decisions for yourself or your buddy. It is a big decision to determine when to safely return to diving. Make that choice with your physician.

Lymphedema

Lymphedema, also known as lymphatic obstruction, is a condition of localized tissue swelling and fluid obstruction caused by a compromised lymphatic system. The condition can be inherited, though it is frequently caused by cancer treatments, and by parasitic infections. In a survey conducted by DAN about breast cancer surgery concerns, 12 percent of the affected divers surveyed reported that diving actually improved their lymphedema symptoms. One diver reported that the lifting of her dive gear made it worse. Compression garments are available to help with swelling if extra care is needed.

---

[48] "DAN Explores Fitness and Diving Issues for Women," www.diversalertnetwork.org/medical/articles/DAN_Explores_Fitness_and_Diving_Issues_for_Women, Donna M. Uguccioni, M.S., DAN Associate Medical Director Dr. Richard Moon, and Dr. Maida Beth Taylor

Osteoporosis and Osteonecrosis

Osteoporosis is "a progressive bone disease that is characterized by a decrease in bone mass and density which can lead to an increased risk of fracture."[49] Osteoporosis causes bones to become weak and brittle. Even mild occurrences like a cough or sneeze can cause a fracture. Bone is living tissue and is continuously being absorbed and then replaced. When the old bone is removed and the new bone isn't regenerated fast enough, then osteoporosis occurs. The decades of the 70s and 80s marked the rise in popularity of sport diving. Women divers who were in their teens and twenties then are now approaching or are in menopause. In the United States, the average age for menopause is 51. True onset of menopause occurs between 50-55 when estrogen depletion occurs in a woman's body. This in turn causes a bone loss of 3-5% per year. Between 60-65 years the risk of fractures increases and continues to rise with age.[50]

Osteonecrosis is a condition noted in divers who experience an infarction in the microcirculation of bone. In this case, the lack of blood flow causes the bone to break down at a frequency that is faster than new bone can be built. The bone begins to die and further break down. Osteoporosis and osteonecrosis can often be confused because of the prefix "osteo," which has its root in the Greek word for bone, but they are not the same in their pathophysiology. Both conditions may increase with advancing age.

Diving with a group or club is a good solution for women who are suffering from physical issues that prevent them from carrying heavy equipment. Dive buddies are willing to help when they understand your physical limits. Photo: Jill Heinerth

At the time of this writing there wasn't any data available in research conducted by DAN. DAN doesn't have a large enough data pool of women who are postmenopausal and with osteoporosis risk or that have significant diving experience to deeper depths that could facilitate an increased risk for osteonecrosis. Regardless, DAN recommends that since women have an increased risk for osteoporosis in general, we should dive more conservatively. This is especially true if women are menopausal or post menopausal because we have estrogen loss during this time that accelerates bone loss.[51] Older women would be better off diving more conservatively to avoid adding osteonecrosis on top of osteoporosis since both are bone damaging dis-

---

[49] Brian K Aldredge; Koda-Kimble, Mary Anne; Young, Lloyd Y.; Wayne A Kradjan; B. Joseph Guglielmo (2009). Applied therapeutics: the clinical use of drugs, Philadelphia: Wolters Kluwer Health/Lippincott Williams & Wilkins, pp 101-3.

[50] Maida Beth Taylor, MD, MPH,FACOG, "Women and Diving: Medical and Health Considerations" in "Women and Pressure", ed. Caroline E. Fife, MD and Marguerite St. Leger Dowse (Plymouth, England: Best Publishing Company, 2010), p 123.

[51] "Osteoporosis," DAN Medical Frequently Asked Questions, www.diversalertnetwork.org/medical/faq/Osteoporosis

eases. Diving is not necessarily contraindicated for women who have osteoporosis. If you have been diagnosed with severe bone loss in your lumbar spine, it is advised to don your cylinders in the water rather than carry them on your back due to the increased risk of a vertebral crush fracture.[52]

If you suffer from osteoporosis or other issues affecting the spine, ask the divemaster if you can take your gear off in the water so they can lift it aboard. It may greatly extend your diving career. Photo: Jill Heinerth

Migraine Headaches

If you suffer from migraines you are not alone. 70% of all migraineurs (migraine sufferers) are women, and 70% report some relationship between a headache and their menstrual cycle. There are steps you can take to relieve or alleviate your migraine headaches. You should contact your physician for the options that would work best for you. DAN says that migraine attacks pose little risk to divers and that's good news. However, if you are experiencing severe and debilitating migraines you should refrain from diving until the symptoms subside. Medications to relieve the pain from a migraine may also "impair performance and judgment, and endanger not only the affected individual, but other accompanying divers."[53]

Cosmetic Plastic Surgery

In 2003 about 87 percent of the cosmetic plastic surgery patients were women. If you're thinking of getting some cosmetic work done and are afraid of the effect on your diving, you'll want to be sure to plan your procedure far enough in advance of any dive excursion to be properly healed. The following wait times before diving are prefaced as recommendations that are based on "favorable, uncomplicated healing."[54] As with any operation or procedure, consult your physician prior to resuming diving.

• Abdominoplasty ("tummy tuck") - about three months

• Breast lift - two to three months

• Breast reduction - two to three months

• Brow lift - six weeks to three months, depending on the procedure

• Otoplasty (ear surgery) - three to six months

[52] Maida Beth Taylor, MD, MPH,FACOG, "Women and Diving: Medical and Health Considerations" in "Women and Pressure", ed. Caroline E. Fife, MD and Marguerite St. Leger Dowse (Plymouth, England: Best Publishing Company, 2010), p. 123

[53] Maida Beth Taylor, MD, MPH,FACOG, "Women and Diving: Medical and Health Considerations" in "Women and Pressure", ed. Caroline E. Fife, MD and Marguerite St. Leger Dowse (Plymouth, England: Best Publishing Company, 2010), p. 95.

[54] www.diversalertnetwork.org/medical/articles/Cosmetic_Plastic_Surgery_and_Diving

- Blepharoplasty (lower eyelid surgery) - about three to six weeks

- Face-lift - about two to three months

- Liposuction - three weeks to three months or longer, depending on the amount of fat tissue removed

- Rhinoplasty ("nose job") - three months

- Botox Injections - Immediately to a week. If the injection was around your mouth, be sure you can orally inflate your BCD and hold a regulator in your mouth and breathe from it comfortably. [55]

Eating Disorders

At least 5 million Americans are affected by anorexia and other eating disorders. But women are 6-10 times likely to experience disordered eating than men. The medications for anorexia nervosa and bulimia nervosa are considered to be contraindications to diving. There is a high psychiatric co-morbidity (two or more coexisting medical conditions or disease processes that are additional to an initial diagnosis)[56] that includes depression, bipolar depressive disorder, personality disorders, obsessive compulsive disorder, anxiety, and phobic disturbances. It is more difficult to distinguish a bulimic person because their BMI is often normal. They may not be good diving candidates due to esophageal dysfunction from induced vomiting or electrolyte disturbances. Anorexics are predisposed to cardiac arrhythmias and sudden death and are therefore not advised to dive. A woman with a low BMI in addition to cold stress during immersion in water greatly intensifies the risk of arrhythmias. "Any woman with a BMI <18 or who is less than 80% of ideal weight should probably not be certified fit to dive." [57] If you suffer from either of these or know someone who is please seek help and get under the care of a physician.

[55] www.diversalertnetwork.org/medical/faq/Botox_Injections

[56] Mosby's Medical Dictionary, 8th Edition, 2009, Elsevier

[57] Maida Beth Taylor, MD, MPH,FACOG, "Women and Diving: Medical and Health Considerations" in "Women and Pressure", ed. Caroline E. Fife, MD and Marguerite St. Leger Dowse (Plymouth, England: Best Publishing Company, 2010), p. 95.

How to rescue a big guy if you are a small woman

It is possible that you will be diving with bigger and stronger people and you might not have the physical reserves to wrangle your partner. As women we may be potentially vulnerable due to smaller size and lessened strength. But, what we don't have in stature and muscle, we can compensate for mentally. Small women should carefully pre visualize strategies for dealing with the rescue of a larger diver. Assess the physicality of the situation and act accordingly. Women are often more capable of multitasking during a rescue if we don't give into our emotions. You might be thinking, "I'm not strong enough... He's too big... I'm too small... I'm not going to be able to help," and so on. Yet, to conduct a successful rescue you must silence those "chattering monkeys" in your head, forcing the emotions to step aside so that you can use intellectual, practical reasoning to solve a problem.

Practice is everything. If you have to rescue a larger unconscious diver, you will need to find a way to manage them and their buoyancy effectively. Photo: Jill Heinerth

According to the Merriam-Webster Dictionary, emotion is "a conscious mental reaction (as anger or fear) subjectively experienced as a strong feeling usually directed toward a specific object and typically accompanied by physiological and behavioral changes in the body." [58] Left unattended these emotions can lead to panic. As the rescuer, that could create a delay in your action and response, or worse. Training and practice can help a diver pattern behavioral responses that become second nature when a real emergency occurs. Repetitive training will help quell the tide of emotions during the response to a stressful incident.

As with any rescue the very first thing to do is to stop and assess the situation and the environment. Is the diver only tired or is he in a full panic? Is there anything around that could make the situation more dangerous for the victim or the rescuer? Things to look for in the open water might include boat traffic, fishing line, rough surf, currents, big waves, depth, threatening sea life or weather. In a cave or wreck, the hazards might include high flow, tight quarters, poor visibility, depth, entanglement, loss of the guideline or possible disorientation. If, and only if, the scene is secure you'll need to decide if you can safely conduct a rescue. Never exceed your limitations of training and risk becoming a victim yourself.

If the victim is merely tired and can follow commands it is a much more manageable situation. He can actually rescue himself. The first thing to do is to slow down. Conduct slow and clear communication either underwater or at the surface. If underwater, try to

58 www.Merriam-Webster.com/dictionary/emotion

solve the problem underwater rather than rushing to the surface. If it is an out of air situation, then deal with it by offering an alternate air source of some kind. If you are a smaller woman then consider using a long 5-foot (1.5m) hose on your primary regulator to keep a victim where you want them. In a real scenario if the diver is truly out of air they will likely grab the regulator from your mouth! If he becomes unconscious, manage the airway the best you can. Consider positioning yourself behind the victim so that you can control buoyancy for both you and the victim as you ascend. You may need to be behind the victim with your knees locked onto the tank for better control. You can hold the tank valve, and keep the airway open by holding the regulator in place while tilting the head back onto your chest or shoulder. Practice this so you will be better prepared should you find yourself in this situation. Wherever you are, on the surface or below, take advantage of physics and use buoyancy, yours and his, to assist you. Try to calm the victim and signal for help. Remember that a tired diver can quickly turn panicked so stay guarded and be prepared. Never get yourself in a position where you could be overpowered by a panicking diver.

Rescuing a rebreather diver has unique challenges. They will have buoyancy in the counterlungs of their rebreather in addition to the wing and perhaps drysuit as well. It all has to be managed carefully to avoid a runaway ascent. Photo: Jill Heinerth

If the victim is truly panicked, he won't follow commands and his behavior will be irrational. Under no circumstances should you get within reach of him. It may be best whether underwater or on the surface to let him exhaust himself. It is possible that he may become so exhausted that he becomes limp and is no longer struggling. Once he has done that you should easily be able to assist him to the surface and or to the shore or boat. Strategy is more important than physical strength underwater since the victim can usually be made weightless. Use the buoyancy control that you have to your advantage. Always signal for assistance even if you don't see anyone because they might see you and come help and call for further assistance. If you need to tow the victim on the surface, your best option may be to tow from behind on the tank valve, the manifold or the wing depending on the gear configuration. Do the best you can without hurting yourself. Realize, too, that the rescue may actually turn into a recovery and it's not your fault. It may be impossible for you to manage someone who is continually fighting you. You'll become overexerted yourself and then be unable to truly assist, possibly causing more harm. Sometimes it might be best to inflate the victim and let him go to the surface. You can perform your normal ascent and catch up with him on the surface to continue the rescue.

If the victim you are attempting to rescue is unconscious on the bottom and you are a smaller woman, you have a challenge. The very worst thing you can do is try to muscle him up by grasping the tank valve and kicking. You'll wear yourself out and probably end up swimming up diagonally instead of directly up. After you've determined he is unresponsive, position him so that his inflator is beside you. If he is face down, grab the tank valve and roll him into this position. From here you have options. Begin to add a little air to both BCDs until the two of you as a unit are neutrally buoyant. If you're having trouble you may need to drop his weight. Be careful while you do this since your ascent may become too rapid. Hopefully you have familiarized yourself with the particular style of inflate/deflate mechanism prior to the dive because you'll need to manage both BCDs while ascending. Remember to keep the airway open while ascending if possible so that any gas in the lungs can escape. Once at the surface inflate both BCDs and continue with the rescue efforts as needed. This shouldn't be a struggle. Use the equipment you have and the laws of physics to assist you.

If you are diving with a rebreather diver for the first time, ask them to demonstrate their inflator mechanism in case it is buried underneath their counterlungs. Further ask them to show you how to close the diver surface valve (DSV) or mouthpiece to prevent flooding, and practice sharing air via their bailout bottle before heading out on a dive together. Don't be shy to ask for a rundown of their unit so you know how to help and how to get air in an emergency. Photo: Jill Heinerth

If you are technical diving and the diver becomes exhausted, confused or incapacitated, you may need to help him through his decompression obligation using your computer for both of you. If computers aren't used then tables will need to be managed. You will become significantly task loaded monitoring depth, time, pressure, gasses, stops and possibly breathing for two people. Being physically tired or nitrogen loaded can compromise constructive decision making. Beware of perceptually narrowing to the point of losing awareness. Keep your head in the game, be intrepid and don't allow yourself to become a victim because you have let yourself be overcome by fear.

A victim in technical gear such as back mounted doubles or a rebreather system can be much larger and bulkier. It may be difficult to work from behind or over the shoulder. You may need to assist an unconscious diver from the front. It goes without saying that these rescue techniques, though taught in an entry level rebreather class, need to be practiced and discussed between dive buddies of dissimilar size. If you are diving with a rebreather partner and are unfamiliar with their equipment you need to know three things: how to inflate the wing, how to close the loop to prevent flooding (makes victim negative), buoyancy and how to find and use the rebreather diver's open circuit bailout gas.

Sadly, there can be gender bias during rescue operations. You might be doing your best assisting in a rescue when someone who thinks they are bigger, stronger or smarter than you are pushes you out of the way to take over. It would be easy to let ego get in the way, but don't turn down assistance and don't take offense. In a rescue situation, people generally just want to help. Getting angry in the moment won't help you or the person you so desperately want to get safely to shore.

The best rescue is the one that is prevented. Most people push themselves far beyond their comfort zone just before they reach panic. All sorts of things can go wrong on any dive no matter the experience level of the diver. The prudent diver should ask themselves this. "At any point on this dive if something were to go wrong can I get myself and any member of the dive team to the surface safely?" Is your answer, "no?" You've heard of listening to your gut, right? This can also be called "woman's intuition." Women are generally in tune with their inner "voice" and are more likely to listen to it if they don't give in to peer pressure. Heed your gut instinct and turn the dive. It may be that you are helping to prevent a problem before it happens and even saving a life.

Women Mentors

Margaret Ross Tolbert - Artist and Environmental Advocate

Margaret Ross Tolbert is a celebrated artist, explorer and author who has combined her love of the water planet with her creative endeavors in an effort to push awareness and conservation initiatives. As an avid snorkeler and freediver, as well as artist who studies the springs for her work, she could not fail to see the changes the freshwater springs near her home in Gainesville, Florida. What she considered timeless treasures were not immune to the vicissitudes and ravages of mankind. She began to see a shifting color palette from blue to green in the paint strokes of her own paintings - a witness to increasing algae and diminished water quality.

This experience sparked a project called AQUIFERious. She gathered art, writing and photography that she and others had created about the springs and solicited contributions from scientists, writers, springs advocates - "those knowledgeable about the springs whose knowledge had set my head on fire." AQUIFERious won a gold medal in non-fiction and silver medal in fine arts in the Florida Book awards (available on Amazon.com).

About 8 years ago, Margaret had an idea that someone dressed for a garden party, Sunday best, or in a Chanel suit would look surreal underwater, underscoring that the springs *are* surreal spaces of color and light, where weightless travel is the norm, the rules of *terra firma* don't seem to apply and where anything seems possible! Her Sirena "sightings" are documented in photography, video, and lenticular and printed photographic images.

Margaret's work is available at a number of galleries, including Thornebrook Galleries in Gainesville, Florida and LeMieux Galleries in New Orleans. News and images of work and installations are posted on her website at margaretrosstolbert.com and also on the Facebook page, Margaret Ross Tolbert artist.

Photos: Top and bottom Tom Morris, Middle Mark Long

Travel Tips for Women

Pre-Trip Planning

Half of the fun of a vacation adventure is in the planning and anticipation. Jill's sister Jan has been known to create chains of paper rings, with each link marking a day prior to departure. Jill invited her on her first diving trip where the two would meet up with other women friends in Mexico's Yucatan Peninsula. Jill had a lot of extra air miles and sent her sister a First Class ticket from Toronto to Cancun where she would pick her up at the airport. Jan meticulously organized her packing, researched the trip and arranged for her husband and kids to take her to the airport some 45 minutes away. The family dropped her on the curb, gave her big hugs and then departed for their own day of fun. Jan approached the ticket counter to check in and gushed with excitement about getting to see her sister Jill. When the ticket agent smiled and asked for her passport, her heart hit the floor. It was on the kitchen counter at home in Markham.

Quick to find a solution, she ran from the check in counter to the curb and hailed a cab. In her enthusiasm, she offered the cabbie extra cash if he would race her home and wait while she grabbed the passport. As they zipped through the streets of Markham, Ontario, she mentally rehearsed her plan to grab the goods. She would sprint from the cab, leaving the door open so he wouldn't drive away with her luggage. Heading to the garden, she would dig under the address sign to uncover the extra house key. Then she would sprint up the steps, open the door and grab the passport.

The cab slowed to a halt and she was already hanging one foot out the door. She ran for the address sign and dug through the half-frozen ground with her bare hands, spraying dirt over the clean white snow. The key was in sight. She pulled it from its Tupperware box and jumped up in excitement. There was still time to make the flight! The next thing she recalls is looking at the crimson red blood on the virginal snow. Forgetting about the address sign and brass bell hanging above, she had nailed her head when standing up. Quickly recovering, she trod into the house, dripping blood up the wooden stairs and tracking mud all the way to the kitchen counter. Without time to leave a note, she ran from the house leaving the mud, blood and debris in her wake.

Surprisingly, she made the flight and connected with Jill in Mexico, a big cut on her forehead, dirty clothes and mud under her fingernails. It was a great start to the trip!

This short chapter delves into some keys tips that will make everything come together even before you leave the house. A little preparation goes a long way to making your vacation come together as smooth as silk.

Booking a Trip

Jill's first diving trip was planned while lounging on the couch at a cottage in Woodland Beach, Ontario. It was a blustery June day, unfit to call summer. She and her dive buddy Kathy huddled under cozy quilts dreaming about warm waters in the tropics. They were leafing through the pages of the "Bible" of all things underwater– *Skin Diver* magazine. The Internet was in its infancy and the dive magazine was the single source for travel information. Both single women, they liked the simplicity of traveling together and sharing a live aboard cabin or hotel room. Through those early trips, they gained enough knowledge and confidence to later travel on their own to diving destinations and have great experiences meeting new people.

If you belong to a club or hang out at a dive shop, they will likely offer trips to interesting destinations. You can travel comfortably as a group in the safety of friends. You'll arrive with dive buddies you trust and have all the details covered by somebody else. Group leaders generally get a free spot for every eight or so divers that they book. Depending on the relationship with the travel wholesaler they may get a kickback of up to 10% of every vacation package (or none), not including flights. If you do the math, that is really not a lot of money. Your group leader is getting a

When traveling with a group, dive gear adds up. Renata Rojas snuggles in with the equipment for a ride from the airport in Nain, Labrador. Photo: Courtesy: www.SednaEpic.com - Jill Heinerth

free trip (not a vacation) and perhaps a little cash, but they will work extremely hard to keep everything on the rails, dealing with any complaints, addressing every diver's equipment needs and acting as a camp counselor. They aren't making a living wage for the time they are absent from their business. These types of bookings offer you terrific value. There is a group leader to cover the frontline of negotiations in the event that you experience problems with travel, dive gear and services, allowing you to relax completely. The downside is cost. There is essentially a retailer and a wholesaler between you and the bottom line. If you are ambitious and confident, you can make your own arrangements and save a lot of money.

Once you have visited a particular destination and wish to travel there again, you will have a good idea of where to find diving services, lodging, meals and other necessities. You may feel comfortable booking directly with the facility. Dive resorts offer package bundles that give you a savings on lodging, meals and diving. Some resorts may even bundle airfares when you live in a gateway city with direct flights to destination. For even more adventurous travelers, you can act as your own travel agent. In the Riviera Maya of Mexico, you can use a website called LocoGringo.com. They represent private homes, condos, motels and lodging in Central America and represent all levels of price points. You can often find an entire home with several bedrooms for the price of a single hotel room at a resort. If you rent your own car, buy a few groceries and grab fills at the local dive shop in Akumal it all adds up to significant savings and you will gain the freedom of keeping your own schedule. If friends can join you, there are noteworthy savings for everyone by sharing the house. Renting homes and condos can be inexpensive and safe at many destinations.

In some cases, you may feel comfortable leaving your arrangements to the last minute. Dive resorts and live aboard dive boats may be willing to give you a big break if you will fill the last cabin or room. If you are a diving professional, they may even offer a courtesy discount of up to 50% off for last minute bookings. This can also be a good solution for a solo traveler trying to escape the single supplemental fee that is often tagged on a cabin with one occupant. They may waive the fee rather than leave the cabin vacant for a cruise.

Women Mentors

Kay Walten - Cave Diving Explorer Turned Travel Entrepreneur

In the mid 90s, Kay Walten moved to Mexico to be closer to the underwater caves she was drawn to explore, but what happened next was an even greater exploration in life.

I never moved to Mexico to start a business. I moved to Mexico to explore caves and live a life of adventure. And I have to say starting my own business has been just that, an adventure. Loco Gringo spring boarded off wanting to guide cave diving groups. Back in 1996, a visiting cave diver mentioned a new thing called the Internet and suggested the idea of offering lodging to visiting cave divers. Exploring caves and guiding divers was great,

Kay Walten exploring the caves of the Riviera Maya in the late 1990s. Photo: Jill Heinerth

but it did not pay the rent. So I bought a used IBM 386 ThinkPad, learned to write HTML and built the first pages of Loco Gringo. I had to go to Tulum each day to send and receive emails to answer questions and help people find the best place for them to stay for their vacation.

I was living in a magical world with the Caribbean in my own backyard. I wanted to share the great things visitors could discover, the people, the culture and my passion for the area. Even today that is a premise for the company.

Loco Gringo became an obsession for me and an exploration project all of its own. LG broke new ground in the Riviera Maya and the Internet. LG was one of the first websites putting out area travel information and vacation rentals. Loco Gringo was one of the first to take payments online, even before the banking industry. Add in the fact that the business was starting in a country that had limited infrastructure, considerations for electric, phone lines, communicating with not only customers but properties, computer parts, tech support, all the day-to-day things businesses needed to be sorted out. It was part of the adventure.

So it was, and still is, an exploration project that never ends. We are always looking into new technologies, ideas, thoughts and processes all to serve our customers.

Having been in business for over 17 years, I look back and yes I sacrificed my passion for cave exploration, for business exploration. However, cave diving, from training to exploration gave me the foundational tools to build on my business exploration and exploration as a person. Cave diving challenged me mentally and physically, unlike anything I had ever experienced.

I stopped cave diving for another reason besides making a living. I stopped cave diving because it stopped being fun. Diving became too goal oriented. We had dives that were dives of a lifetime and because the results of those dives did not meet the objective, the dive was looked upon as a failure. In retrospect that is a shame because the dives were incredible. Being in the moment and appreciating where I was and what I was doing was lost on how much line was still on my reel, what wasn't achieved or other frustrations.

The theme of goal orientation is not a new thing in my life, I do thrive on achieving, but I have had to learn to step back and appreciate what I am actually doing, rather than to have everything ride on the end result.

There has to be a balance in everything we do in life. I always said anything worth doing, is worth doing to an extreme. That concept is flawed. Doing one thing to an extreme is not sustainable, and we miss out on other aspects of life at the same time. Balance in our work, play, passion, family gives us a better rounded life experience.

The other thing I believe is that women have to put themselves first. We tend to put ourselves at the end of the list and fail to respect our needs, wants, desires, dreams, etc. We need to put ourselves at the top of the list and be true to ourselves. The right people and the right opportunities will then come to fulfill us.

Today Kay's work extends far beyond her business pursuits. She has been clowning around with Patch Adams in Guatemala in hospitals and orphanages, working with the Humane Society International in Africa and empowering women in Tanzania by providing sewing machines and entrepreneurial coaching. She is also a motivational writer for the Indrani's Light Foundation in Houston. This organization was established as a non-profit helping women take steps to "Live a Brighter Life." Kay is an inaugural inductee in the Women Divers Hall of Fame and is responsible for tens of thousands of feet of original exploration in caves of the Riviera Maya in Mexico.

Packing

A simple task like packing for a trip has become a chore due to TSA regulations, weight limitations and rules for hazardous goods. The first step is to check your airline and fully digest the rules for baggage. Determine whether you will be allowed one carry-on and a personal item or only a single carry-on bag. Inquire about whether that has a weight limit since some airlines will weigh you and your bag to properly pack a small plane. Then learn about the checked baggage rules and fees. Most airlines charge additional fees for baggage and some of these fees can be very steep. If you check excess or go overweight it is possible to accrue fees of hundreds or even thousands of dollars. Jill once paid an unavoidable extra baggage bill of $3700 for a single flight! She was carrying filming equipment and the airline had a baggage embargo that limited each traveler to a solitary bag.

Consider pre-shipping goods through cargo, delivery services or the post office. But if that's not possible, there are some ways to avoid additional fees for checked bags on airlines. Frequent flyers are usually rewarded with free baggage allowances. First class passengers also have more liberal limits. Sometimes it is worth the upgraded ticket price to take advantage of the weight or piece bonus. Airline credit cards also offer free baggage perks and coupons from time to time. Working journalists may also find a media rate discount available to them on some airlines. You can also check with your airline on the day of travel to see if they have a discounted First Class upgrade package for any available seats. If you do this before check in, you will also get the advantage of the baggage allowances that come with the seat.

Sometimes pre-shipping equipment is a good solution. A pallet of gear may be easier and cheaper to transport via cargo or delivery service than traveling with the same equipment on the airlines. Photo: Courtesy www.SednaEpic.com - Jill Heinerth

When you pack your carry-on and checked luggage, make it easy to inspect and difficult for little pieces to fall out and be lost or pilfered. Use travel organizer bags or zippered bags to compartmentalize your items. Make sure you have not packed so tight that it will be difficult for an inspector to close the bag or case. They are in a hurry and if something is hanging out the edge, they might damaged or lose it. Wear or carry-on your most expensive items such as a diving computer or camera system. (That's why Jill loves her fully capable watch-sized computers from Suunto. They are fully functional and totally wearable). Jill once wore an 80 pound parka to a job in Russia. Half of her camera system components and regulators were packed away in the pockets. A security agent in Heathrow Airport gave her a bit of a hard time when passing through security but could not find any regulations that would prevent her from wearing heavy clothing.

If you use a small airport, remember the carry-on may have to be gate checked and will be out of your possession for the duration of the flight. It will get a little bit of handling and should be packed and padded appropriately. There are a few items that have extra cautions associated with them. Large lithium batteries that run scooters may be beyond the acceptable limit of lithium content for a passenger aircraft. Sometimes airlines will also restrict the number of spare lithium batteries that you are allowed to carry either in personal carry-ons or checked baggage. This includes small batteries that power lights and cameras. Other items such as Sofnolime for rebreathers should be accompanied by a Materials Safety Data Sheet (MSDS) and placed in checked baggage only.

Passing through the security checkpoint may also present some issues. Ensure your carry-on is within any weight and size limits and packed according to regulations. Any gels or liquids will need to be carried according to current standards (currently one ounce each of up to three items and sealed in a clear Ziplock baggie). You will probably need to remove your shoes, so wear socks so you are not left walking across a dirty floor in bare feet. Head coverings may need to be removed as well as jackets.

Airport Security

If you are pulled aside for a further security check, it is your right to request that the search is conducted by a woman. The authors have experienced some pat-downs that made them blush, especially in front of a large crowd of travelers. Although it might be embarrassing, you may feel more secure knowing that any issues can be witnessed and verified by a crowd. With the technology available at airports today, they still seem to cross the physical line with many modest passengers. We really miss the days when we were actually treated like customers.

There are a few things you can do to increase your personal safety and comfort in the screening line. Loose fitting clothes and comfortable shoes will feel great on the plane and draw less attention getting there. If you are uncomfortable with a pat-down or enhanced screening, ask for a supervisor. If a pat-down is required in order to complete screening:

Expedition Leader Susan Eaton arrives in Labrador at the start of the Sedna Epic Expedition. The project presented daunting challenges for transporting gear and personnel to the Arctic; a job that took her over a year to coordinate. Photo: Courtesy www.SednaEpic.com - Jill Heinerth

• It should be conducted by an officer of the same gender, although you might have to wait for one to become available.

• You can request a private screening at any time and it should be offered when the officer must pat-down sensitive areas. During a private screening, another TSA employee should be present and you have a right to be accompanied by a companion of your choice.

• You may ask for a chair if you need to sit down.

• You should inform an officer before the pat-down begins of any difficulty raising your arms, remaining in the position required for a pat-down, or any areas of the body that are painful or sensitive when touched.

• You should not be asked to remove or lift any article of clothing to reveal a sensitive body area.

In addition to the pat-down, a TSA officer may use technology to test for traces of explosive material. If explosive material is detected, you will have to undergo additional screening.

If a request by a screener offends your sensibility, religious/cultural traditions or violates your rights as a disabled person, politely ask for a supervisor. If someone has crossed the line, report it immediately here: http://www.justice.gov/crt/complaint/#two.

Some other resources include:

Disabled passenger complaints: TSA-ContactCenter@dhs.gov

Lost or damaged property: http://www.tsa.gov/traveler-information/claims-management-branch

Civil rights and multicultural issues direct email: TSA-CRL@tsa.dhs.gov

The best advice is to avoid the enhanced pat-down in the first place. According to the TSA, the most important preventive action is to avoid wearing or carrying items that will trigger the metal detector or other scanning devices. To reduce this circumstance, you should take everything out of your pockets (including lint) before you go through screening. Also, when traveling, avoid wearing clothes with a high metal content and put heavy jewelry and dive computer watches on only after you go through security.

The TSA has a help line to assist travelers with disabilities and medical conditions. They recommend that passengers call 72 hours ahead of travel for information about what to expect during screening at 1-855-787-2227. Travelers may also request a Passenger Support Specialist ahead of time by calling the TSA Cares help line. The hours of operation for the help line are Monday through Friday 8 a.m. – 11 p.m. EST and weekends and Holidays 9 a.m. – 8 p.m. EST. Travelers who are deaf or hard of hearing can use a relay service to contact TSA Cares or can e-mail: TSA-ContactCenter@dhs.gov.

Personal Security

Women need to be extra vigilant when traveling, especially if they are alone or in small groups. Not all societies share our best attempts at gender equality! If you are alone, you'll need to stay low key and keep your head on a swivel in some places. Common sense is your best ally.

Carry a small amount of cash in a throw-away wallet or billfold. If you are ever mugged, you can toss it on the ground and run. Keep your passport separate and secure and don't assume that you are the only one who can enter your room safe. Make a photocopy of your passport to leave at home and one to carry separate from the passport in case of loss. Jill made it home without a passport after it was stolen in Mexico. Knowing the number likely saved her a lot of aggravation.

Don't carry a purse that can be easily snatched from your shoulder. A small waist pack, backpack or cross shoulder bag is more secure. PacSafe makes a line of bags that are attractive, functional and have a secure mesh that cannot be sliced open with a knife. Belts and body packs can be worn under clothing, but be aware on subways and buses where people can snag your cash when they are in close contact.

There are a few small waterproof bags and mini cases that will allow you to take precious items with you underwater. If you are not positive about the security of items on the boat, or if you are shore diving, these can be life savers.

When using taxis, get some advice before you reach your destination. Find out who operates the trusted cab services and whether there are any other organizations to stay away from. When working on a Hollywood movie in Romania, Jill was warned not to use the taxis of a certain color. They were operated by a conglomerate of petty thieves. Sure enough, when her dive buddy Brian arrived in Bucharest, he grabbed the wrong cab. The taxi got him to the hotel but dropped him at the back loading dock only after taking all his money.

In both Romania and Italy Jill has been asked for her passport as she leisurely walked through the busy streets. In both cases, a rather official looking person strode up to her purposefully, loudly demanding her passport. Jill told them to "bugger off," knowing she was only moments away from having it snatched. In another case, she was stopped by a woman pushing a map towards her face while she asked for help in broken English. When she saw a band of small kids running towards her in her peripheral vision, she knew she was about to be mugged. She yelled out to gather attention and ran off successfully. The pursuing children were called off with a loud whistle by their handler. A trusting person, her first gut reaction was to try to be polite, but unfortunately, there are many people who will take advantage of your disorientation in a new location.

If you decide to enjoy the nightlife at any destination, take a friend and never leave your drink unattended. Watch the bartender make it or better yet, order something that comes straight out of a bottle or can. Even in the US, women are drugged and raped at an alarming frequency after their drinks are laced with powerful drugs.

Cultural Sensitivity

In general, it is not too worrying to travel to a sunny Caribbean diving resort, but the world is now open to us and traveling to exotic corners of the planet is easy. If you are going off the beaten track, register your plans with your country's consulate. Keep their number handy in case you need help. In many cases it is far better to call the

Research your destination before jumping on the plane. It is important to be culturally sensitive to the local customs. In the Western Desert of North Africa, it was important for Jill to remain properly covered in order to gain the respect of local Amazigh Berbers. Photo: Robert McClellan

consulate first before attempting to contact the police. Although you may feel like a victim, the police may have different cultural biases. A woman raped in some countries is not a victim. She can be jailed, stoned or put to death for crimes of adultery.

No woman deserves to be leered at, abused or raped, but there are many cultures who believe that a woman dressed in a particular way is "asking for it." Do a little research ahead of time about cultural sensitivities in the region you are visiting. When Jill led an expedition to a remote corner of Egypt, she knew she would be interacting with Amazigh Berbers as well as conservative Egyptians. She researched as much as possible ahead of time about how to cover her head, how to dress and how to speak to men. Once she arrived at her destination, she continued to ask her trusted Egyptian colleagues to let her know if she was doing anything that could be considered improper. They were very pleased that this concerned her and it helped strike a real friendship of mutual respect.

Being culturally sensitive may mean staying well covered on a dive boat. It may mean traveling to the souvenir shops with a male companion. It may include wearing a head covering or long pants/skirt in a church or addressing men in a particular way. It also means making a good effort at attempting to use the local language. At the very least, learn how to speak "menu." Be able to order food politely and thank a hostess. Learn the words for "help" and "can you help me?" Be able to ask for the location of the bathroom and apologize for not speaking the local language. Just trying to make an effort at conversation goes a long way.

Nitty Gritty

When you are doing your pre-trip research, find out about the toilet habits of the population or you might be in for a surprise. You may want to carry a good supply of toilet paper and some small change to gain access to a restroom. You might consider taking a "Lady Jane" or "Pee Funnel," which will permit you to pee while standing. Carry it in a Ziplock bag with some moist wipes so you can clean it and put it away in a sanitary manner. Many destinations have poor excuses for toilets and some only filthy holes in the floor that might fit your worst nightmare scenario. For this reason and so many others, listen to your mother's advice– wear a proper pair of shoes, not flip flops.

Communicating with the outside world might also be challenging at some destinations. Discover whether your cell phone will work and what fees you might incur. International cell phone calls may be billed at many dollars per minute. Data might be a better option, but your phone may need GSM capability or an international data plan. You may be able to use a relay service such as Google Voice or Skype to make calls using data instead of expensive phone time. Phone cards are also an option in many countries. These can be used on land lines at reasonable rates, especially when Internet connectivity is not available or cyber security is questionable.

If you are not planning to use your phone, make sure you either put it in airplane mode or turn it off to avoid excessive international roaming fees. A short trip can result in hundreds if not thousands of dollars of unexpected fees, from forgetting to disable data roaming!

Research the local power supply before traveling to ensure you have the right connections for charging your dive light, cell phone or laptop. Even destinations with similar 110V power as the United States may require adapters for devices that have grounding plugs. It is common in Central America to find only two-pronged outlets.

Cheater plugs are worth their weight in gold in places such as Mexico.

Cyber security is another issue to be aware of when traveling. Open networks in coffee shops and airports might be free but may leave your computer vulnerable if you have left yourself open to attack. Learn more about how to safely browse in open networks. Cyber cafes allow patrons to use the house computer, but it may be tracking your keystrokes too. Use house computers for only necessary functions and nothing that can compromise your banking data. Clear the cache and shut down the browser after your session is finished. Protect credit cards and passports from electronic theft with a secure wallet or aluminum foil. Criminals can steal electronic data using a device pointed at your backpack or purse and you might not even know you have been compromised. Check your credit card and bank statements immediately after arriving home, using a secure connection.

It is a good idea to pay with cash in unfamiliar restaurants rather than give up your credit card to be carried away by a waiter. The United States will soon catch up to the rest of the world and start requiring the use of chip credit cards. The good news is that the waiter will be able to bring a credit card device to your table to complete a transaction rather that take your card out of your site to scan it. There is a lot of personal information on your credit card's magnetic strip and thieves pay a lot of money for that data, which can be swiped in a moment. Similarly, do not let your passport leave your control. If a hotel clerk asks to retain your passport, decline to provide it. There is a lot of personal data stored in new e-Passports and that data can compromise your identity. The physical passport itself also has a lot of value and losing it can create a nightmare that lasts for years. When backpacking through Greece as a young student, Jill naively gave her passport to a demanding hostel clerk who stored the passports in the facility's safe. She tried to check out of the flea infested dungeon for three days, but the clerk told her he had no access to the safe during that time. Being a lone female traveler, she was reluctant to call the police and start a problem. Finally after she told them that she did not have any more money for the hostel accommodation, they gave her back her passport!

Traveling is incredibly rewarding and learning about other cultures is exciting. If you do a little research ahead of time, and conduct your activities carefully, your trip will be more enjoyable and safe.

Career Profiles in Diving

Catherine Botalla and the Development Team at AquaLung

Catherine Botalla has worked in purchasing and development of neoprene products with the Aqualung brand since 1998. Several years ago, she was tasked with the job of creating an entirely new line of equipment specifically to meet the needs of women divers. She assembled an international group of women and spent two years in the engineering, development and testing of completely new gear. Their collective work resulted in the Aqualung women's line. Beyond terrific new styling and colors, they identified over 20 unique innovations that would make women's gear more comfortable and stylish. In Europe, they tested magnetic closures for wetsuit necklines that would protect women's hair. They created a double lipped mask skirt that prevented red marks from pressure. They

added a unique optional lip guard to regulator mouthpieces so that women in cold water would be more comfortable. On top of that, each piece of neoprene was re-examined and tailored to optimize fit and account for the unique proportions of women. We salute the women at Aqualung who have forged successful careers in engineering, product development, sales and marketing.

Women Mentors

Dr. Dawn Kernagis - Researcher

As the U.S. Navy Undersea Medicine Program's first Predoctoral Award recipient, Dr. Dawn Kernagis obtained her Ph.D. at Duke University while identifying how genetics influence susceptibility to decompression sickness. Her current research is supported by the Office of Naval Research and the American Heart Association and is focused on developing therapeutics in the setting of brain injury, including CNS decompression sickness and oxygen toxicity in divers.

Dawn started her diving career in 1993 at the age of 15. Her greatest challenge as a young female technical and cave diver in the mid 90's was the small number of female colleagues and mentors that were available at that time. Her male colleagues were excellent teachers and teammates, but she always craved having female perspective. Dawn

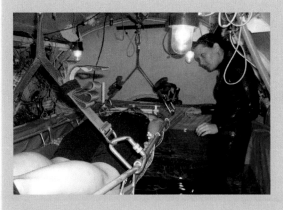

has experienced and learned the importance of being patient with training believing that time, subsequent experience and comfort in the water are far more important than any certification card or fancy piece of equipment. Her advice is to "surround yourself with teammates who have the same mentality and find good mentors along the way." She was lucky to have incredible mentors from her open water days onward, and she also made sure that she learned everything possible about diving (and life!) from these mentors along the way.

Over the years, Dawn has worked as a diver, coordinator, and consultant on a number of international wreck and cave exploration projects, including the record breaking deep cave exploration efforts of the Woodville Karst Plain Project, from 1996-2007. Prior to graduate school, Dawn conducted physiology research for the U.S. Navy, DAN, and NASA.

Dawn is a remarkable biomedical researcher, woman and diver and she offers some sage advice. "No dive is worth dying for. Never be afraid to say that something doesn't feel right or you are not comfortable with a dive plan (or even in the middle of the dive itself). The women I look up to the most in diving have all called dives, even the biggest dives with media coverage or a huge team involved, and I am sure they are still here for that very reason. I've heard too many stories of dives going bad, sometimes even ending in an accident, where someone didn't listen to their gut."

Dawn is also the founder of Project Pink Tank, a dive industry-sponsored study that is focused on creating a better understanding of diver health outcomes among cancer survivors.

For further information and to donate to Project Pink Tanks please visit: http://rubicon-foundation.org/Projects/project-pink-tank/

Career Opportunities

Finding a Career in the Underwater World

Many of us knew quite early in our diving careers that we wanted to find a way to turn our passion into a vocation. The challenge lies in plotting a course that helps you gain experience while sustaining yourself. There are many possible directions to take to get involved in an underwater career and many mentors to reach out to. Following are numerous online resources and scholarship opportunities for divers, but don't be afraid to be less conventional. Find someone you admire and reach out to ask for a gig or ask for help. The links were correct at the time of printing, and further information about various organizations has been added to assist you in case links are changed at a later date.

Dive Leadership and Instruction

Dive leadership and instruction often come to mind for people who are seeking careers in the underwater world. Dive shops and resorts worldwide are in need of professionally qualified divemasters, instructors and boat crew to serve their operations. Retail operations and online stores seek sales people, marketing experts and service technicians. Training agencies such as PADI offer career listings for their professional members. Attending diving shows such as the Diving Equipment and Marketing Association's (DEMA) annual trade show might also give you a chance to meet prospective employers face to face.

Dive leadership is one of the most common ways that people make a career in the underwater world. Divemasters, instructors, and crew are integral to retail and resort operations around the world. There are many opportunities to work and travel for women with professional credentials. Photo: Courtesy of Aqualung

If you apply to a resort or dive shop directly, remember that these facilities may receive hundreds of applications for work. Every application will be accompanied by a long list of diving credentials. Remember, those credentials, though hard won, are the baseline for entry. You are not unique in those qualifications. It is very important to highlight your abilities outside of diving. Are you a good salesperson, cook, boat captain, yoga instructor or marine mechanic? Are you a good team player? Are you versatile and able to take on whatever tasks are needed for a particular operation, even if that means painting the walls or cleaning toilets? Skills outside of diving are what will separate you from the pack and make you unique and valuable.

Teaching can be group focused or private. You can work for an organization or build your own entrepreneurial business where you specialize in a unique aspect of diving.

Career Profiles in Diving

Nancy Easterbrook, Technical Diving Entrepreneur, Women Divers Hall of Fame 2012

Nancy started diving in 1973, got the bug and diving became a passion. At a time when technical diving was still in its infancy, she moved with her 2 children Brandee & Walker to Grand Cayman in 1994 and launched her business Divetech. She is a pioneer in technical diving, rebreathers and the sport of breath-hold freediving in Cayman. When she first arrived on the island, strict rules prohibiting technical diving pursuits had to be overcome. She took on the challenge and

Divetech Grand Cayman. Photo: Jill Heinerth

changed the culture of diving with a great track record of safety. She founded the Innerspace event, which brings together CCR divers from around the world to share knowledge and friendship. She has devoted the past 20 years to exploring all that diving has to offer and has championed many causes for environmental awareness in the marine and terrestrial environment. A recent achievement was an 8-year project to bring the USS Kittiwake to Cayman as an artificial reef.

Andrea Zaferes, Women Divers Hall of Fame 2000

Andrea teaches over 1000 police, fire, EMS and sport divers worldwide on an annual basis in everything from underwater vehicle extrication, sport diving rescue, and field neurological evaluations, to homicidal drowning investigations. She is Vice President of Lifeguard Systems and RIPTIDE, a course director, instructor trainer, well-published author, noted public speaker, award winner, magazine editor, on-line discussion group manager and one of the leading trainers in the water rescue and recovery industry today.

Marine Biology

Marine biology encompasses the study of marine organisms, their behaviors, and their interactions with the environment. By studying marine organisms, you may be led to investigate fish farms, new medical compounds, global climate change or biotechnology. Graduates with marine science degrees may work for governments, educational institutions, defense contractors, space agencies, engineering firms, chemical manufacturers, non-governmental organizations such as Greenpeace or other interest and advocacy groups.

Marine Biologist and Aquarist Ruby Banwait working with children in Labrador with her mini-aquarium program that brings kids close to their local marine life. Photo: Courtesy www.SednaEpic.com - Jill Heinerth

Career Profiles in Diving

Eugenie Clark, Ph.D. - Ichthyologist, Women Divers Hall of Fame 2000

Dr. Eugenie Clark is a pioneering ichthyologist with a special interest in sharks. She has served at great institutions such as Scripps Institution of Oceanography, the New York Zoological Society, the American Museum of Natural History, and the Mote Marine Laboratory. Eugenie's work has inspired the next generation to become active protectors of sharks. She has authored numerous books and over 160 scientific papers, holds three honorary degrees, and has received awards from National Geographic, the Explorers Club and the Underwater Society of America. She is currently a Senior Research Scientist at the University of Maryland.

Holly Martel Bourbon, Women Divers Hall of Fame 2007

Holly Martel Bourbon is Curator of Fishes/Diving Safety Officer for the National Aquarium in Baltimore, MD. In this position, Bourbon manages the fish, invertebrates and elasmobranchs in the Aquarium's collection. From 2006-2012, she was the Diving Safety Officer/Biologist at the Massachusetts Division of Marine Fisheries primarily focusing on research diving in local waters. Holly began her career as a diving marine scientist as a member of the New England Aquarium dive team in 1985. She was a Senior Aquarist/ Dive Safety Officer at New England Aquarium from 1987-2005.

Holly has a long history of public service, developing innovative marine conservation and education programs utilizing her underwater expertise. Her deep commitment to the environment is evident through her work with various conservation groups such as REEF, the New England Aquarium, the Bahama Conservation Group and other conservation oriented NGOs.

Holly's advice to women interested in following in her fin-steps is this: "Never underestimate the value of volunteering or pursuing an internship. I hadn't considered a marine biology profession (wanted to be a large animal veterinarian like James Herriot) until I pursued a required internship while I was a sophomore at Mount Holyoke College in South Hadley, Massachusettes. The New England Aquarium was listed in our Career Services booklet. I thought working with penguins, sea turtles and otters would be something different."

"The diving for me didn't come until later (once I realized I loved the fact that I could couple diving with my love of animals). Once I started diving, I naturally ventured towards teaching and being a diving instructor. Diving Safety Officer positions, especially for women, are finally starting to blossom as more aquariums open and offer diving programs. My position is unusual in that I combine my two loves, animal/husbandry care and diving safety. Although challenging, this dual role allows me to not only keep the animals I care for safe but also the dive staff and volunteers safe in their work."

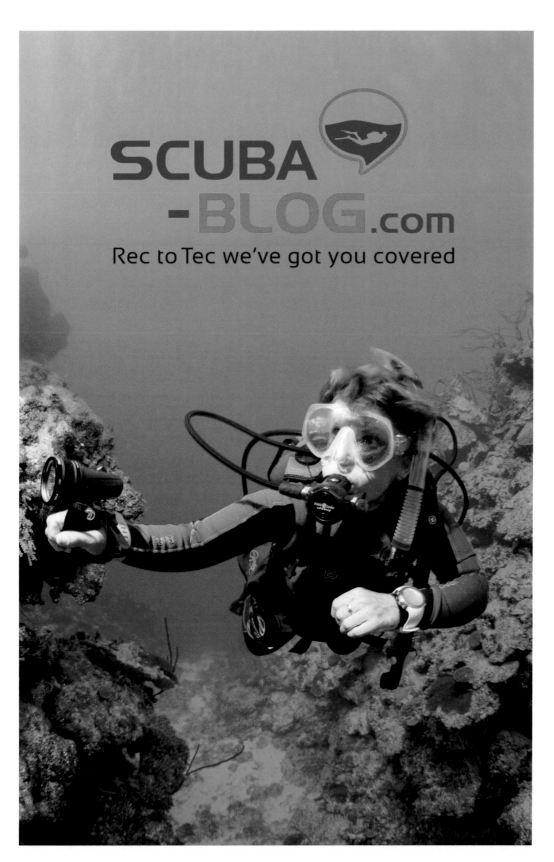

Emma L. Hickerson - Marine Researcher, Women Divers Hall of Fame 2014

Emma has held the position of Research Coordinator for National Oceanic and Atmospheric Administration's (NOAA) Flower Garden Banks National Marine Sanctuary (FGBNMS) since 1997. During this time she has contributed to over 40 scientific publications relating to the marine environment. She has served as the Unit Diving Supervisor for NOAA's FGBNMS dive unit since 2005, and has supervised over 5000 dives during over 155 sanctuary research cruises. She has coordinated and led research utilizing SCUBA, remotely operated vehicles, and manned submersibles. She is not only passionate about studying and protecting the marine environment, but also interpreting science through multimedia, including photography, videography and art.

Shirley Pomponi, Ph.D., Women Divers Hall of Fame 2003

Dr. Shirley Pomponi is Executive Director of the NOAA Cooperative Institute for Ocean Exploration, Research, and Technology at Harbor Branch Oceanographic Institute, Florida Atlantic University in Fort Pierce, Florida. Her research focuses on marine biotechnology, in general, and the discovery and development of marine-derived drugs, in particular. She has authored or co-authored more than 100 scientific publications and is co-inventor on several patents. An explorer at heart, Dr. Pomponi has led numerous research expeditions worldwide. She has discovered many deepwater sponges from which chemicals with pharmaceutical properties have been identified. A highlight of her career is the opportunity she's had to make more than 300 dives in the Johnson-Sea-Link submersibles—piloted by her husband, Don Liberatore—and she continues to enjoy SCUBA diving for science and pleasure. Shirley continues voluntary work in many areas. She is President of the Southern Association of Marine Laboratories and Chair of the Florida Institute of Oceanography. She is a member of the Board of Trustees of the Consortium for Ocean Leadership, the Florida Oceans and Coastal Council, the U.S. National Committee for the Census of Marine Life, the National Association of Marine Laboratories, the Southeast Coastal Ocean Observing Regional Association, and the Florida Ocean Alliance.

Oceanography and Engineering

Oceanographers provide services extending beyond the study of marine organisms and their work is often integrated with that of marine biologists. The discipline of oceanography includes specialists in geology, engineering, chemistry, climatology and other areas. Marine engineering may further encompass equipment design and other technical areas. Oceanographers and engineers predict climate change, design submersibles, track pollution, measure seafloor movement, design remediation strategies for oil spills, work with computers and engineer tools for researchers. Oceanographers work for public institutions and major corporations but some are entrepreneurial inventors whose ideas solve problems in the marine environment.

Career Profiles in Diving

Tamara "Tammy" Brown - Commercial Diving Educator, Women Divers Hall of Fame 2000

Tammy Brown, President and CEO of Divers Academy International, began her career in Commercial Diving in 1982, after graduating from what was then Divers Academy of the Eastern Seaboard. Tammy earned many advanced certifications in related fields, such as bridge inspection and nondestructive testing. She also became active with the Accrediting Commission for Career Schools and Colleges of Technology, serving as a Management Specialist and a Team Leader.

Becoming Divers Academy's School Director in 1990, she also took on the role as President of the Association of Commercial Diving Educators. In this role, she was one of the pioneers in developing commercial diving certification standards, and went on to have those standards become accredited by the American National Standards Institute (ANSI). To this day, Tammy is recognized as a leader in the commercial diving industry.

Now as President and CEO of the renamed Divers Academy International, she has greatly expanded operations. Tammy built an advanced curriculum and purchased a nearly 300 foot (90m) deep quarry in Allentown, PA where students train to the highest deep dive international standard with curriculum options in Welding Technologies or Deep Dive Mixed Gas specialty programs.

Dr. Kathryn D.Sullivan - Astronaut, Women Divers Hall of Fame 2008

Dr. Kathryn Sullivan is the first American woman to walk in space. She is a veteran of three shuttle missions and a 2004 inductee to the Astronaut Hall of Fame. Dr. Sullivan left NASA to accept a Presidential appointment to the post of Chief Scientist at the NOAA. Here she oversaw a wide array of research and technology programs ranging from climate and global change to satellites and marine biodiversity. Dr. Sullivan served on the Pew Oceans Commission, whose nationwide study and subsequent report, "America's Living Oceans: Charting a Course for Sea Change," called for immediate reform of U.S. ocean laws and policies to avert the decline of ocean wildlife and collapse of ocean ecosystems (2000-2003). She was an oceanography officer in the U.S. Naval Reserve from 1988-2006 and served on the Chief of Naval Operations Executive Panel from 1988-1996. She is a member of the Woods Hole Oceanographic Institution, the Explorers Club, the Society of Woman Geographers and Association of Space Explorers. Dr. Sullivan served as President and CEO of Center of Science & Industry (COSI) in Columbus, Ohio. COSI is one of the nation's premier centers for hands-on, inquiry-based science learning resources. Dr. Sullivan is currently Director of the Battelle Center for Mathematics & Science Education Policy in the John Glenn School of Public Affairs at the Ohio State University.

Astrobiologist Dr. Jenn Macalady is assisted by Nikita Shiel-Rolle. Dr. Macalady studies unique biofilms and algal matts that reside in remote underwater caves. Her work leads us to a better understanding of how life can exist in extreme environments such as space. Photo: Jill Heinerth

Other Careers

There are many jobs in the underwater world that do not fit into the categories of marine biology, oceanography or ocean engineering. These jobs may fit more than one category, or they may overlap other fields, such as education, communication, economics, seagoing careers, military careers or entrepreneurship. These jobs may require vastly different educational and experience backgrounds. There are countless possibilities for a water-related career: educator, writer, filmmaker, photographer, ecotourism guide, park ranger, beach superintendent, aquarist, environmental lawyer, environmental advocate, policy expert, veterinarian, economist, archaeologist, historian, fundraiser, spokesperson, aquaculturist, manager of an NGO, marina operations, boat captain/crew, environmental planner, computer specialist, ecologist, hatchery specialist, landscape or maritime architect and more.

It is common for people who work in the underwater world to create a hybrid career with many different facets. A diving instructor may also shoot videos for their customers. A researcher may additionally collect unique fish species for aquariums or institutions. A boat captain may operate a diving lodge and an environmental lawyer may also be involved with an NGO.

Career Profiles in Diving

CDR Darlene M. Iskra, USN (ret), Ph.D., Women Divers Hall of Fame 2008

CDR Iskra entered the Navy via Officer Candidate School in March 1979. After completing the Naval School of Diving and Salvage in Washington, D.C. as one of the first female Special Operations Officers, she reported to her first ship, the USS Hector (AR-7) in December 1980. As Diving Officer for the Hector, the only Navy dive locker in northern California, she was responsible for the underwater ship's husbandry of Navy surface ships stationed throughout the San Francisco Bay Area and beyond. During that two year tour, she supervised all of the ship's underwater husbandry operations; conducted the first underwater propeller change overseas, in Yokosuka harbor, Japan; conducted underwater ship repairs and security swims for the USS Kennedy Carrier Battle Group in Mombasa harbor, Kenya; and successfully ensured the certification of the dive boat's portable surface supplied air system.

During her 21 years in the Navy, she served on four different salvage ships, the USS Grasp (ARS-51), the USS Preserver (ARS-8), the USS Hoist (ARS-40), and the USS Opportune (ARS-41) where she served as Commanding Officer (1990-1993), the first woman to command a commissioned vessel. Throughout her shipboard tours, she was on hand during all diving evolutions, from training to operational dives. While in command, her crew participated in clean-up after Hurricane Andrew devastated the Miami area in 1992. She retired from the Navy in April 2000. After her retirement, she attended graduate school at the University of Maryland, College Park and received her Ph.D. in Sociology in December 2007, specializing in Military and Gender, Work and Family.

CAPT Diann Karin Lynn, Women Divers Hall of Fame 2000

Karin is a former U.S. Navy captain who retired from a 30-year career in civil and ocean engineering for the Navy in 2007. She has an MS in Ocean Engineering from the University of Hawaii, and she was honored to be among the first female graduates of the Navy's deep-sea diving school in 1983. From there she went on to specialize in diving and underwater systems, and among other assignments was the head of the Navy's Ocean Facilities Program, where she oversaw about 250 professional military divers and ocean engineers worldwide. She keeps her marine science credentials active as an energetic member of ocean-related professional associations and activities.

Janice Raber, Women Divers Hall of Fame 2001

Janice is a great example of how public service and the spirit of volunteerism can open doorways. Rather than waiting for opportunities to present themselves, Janice made them. She is a Trustee of the Long Island Divers Association and has served as an officer in various capacities as well as co-producer of their annual film festival. She's been diving since 1986, is an instructor, active member of two dive clubs and has served on the Suffolk County Leisure Services Advisory Board. Janice's efforts opened 15 county and state park dive sites, fostered the purchase of a historic shipwreck site, and helped designate two local marine parks. She arranges beach cleanups, fund-raisers, seminars and exhibits at dive expos, museums and public functions. A member of the New York State Outdoor Writers Association, Janice has published over one hundred dive articles and is a regular contributor to Long Island Boating World.

Barbara "Bobbie" Scholley, CAPT (ret), USN, Women Divers Hall of Fame 2000

Bobbie retired from the U.S. Navy in 2005 after 25 years of service. As a Diving and Salvage officer since 1983, she had key leadership roles in many Navy Diving Operations including the TWA Flight 800 recovery in 1996, the USS Cole bombing recovery in 2000 and USS Monitor Expeditions 2001 and 2002. She has 19 surface supplied mixed gas dives to 240 feet on the USS Monitor. Bobbie served in three Commanding Officer positions, USS Bolster (ARS 38), a diving and salvage ship; Mobile Diving and Salvage Unit Two; and Naval Weapons Station, Earle, NJ. She was also the U.S. Navy's Supervisor of Diving from 1997-1999. She has an MS in National Resource Strategies from the Industrial College of the Armed Forces and an honorary Doctorate of Science from Illinois State University (ISU). She is a member of ISU's College of Science and Arts Hall of Fame and currently does consulting work.

Dr. Marguerite St. Leger Dowse, Women Divers Hall of Fame 2000

Marguerite has been associated with the Diving Diseases Research Centre (DDRC) in the UK since 1989 and specializes in field data – real world information from divers – until recently focusing on the effects of diving on women. Other topics have included diving and asthma, diving with diabetes, reverse dive profiles and flying after treatment for DCI. She was awarded the British Sub Aqua Club (BSAC) Duke of Edinburgh Prize for research in 1994 and again in 2006, being the only person to awarded the accolade twice. In 2006 she received the European Underwater and Baromedical Society's Zetterstrom Award. Current research projects include studies into the general health of divers which also looks at the use of physician prescribed, over the counter, and recreational drug use in divers; a separate study is investigating the reasons for delay in seeking help and treatment for decompression illness.

Resources for Information on Marine Careers

Woods Hole Oceanographic Institution (WHOI)

www.marinecareers.net

The most comprehensive website for information about marine careers is compiled by the Woods Hole Oceanographic Institution (WHOI) through their Sea Grant Program. The site describes various career fields, offers information on salary potential and includes examples of successful people working in marine careers.

Oceanlink

http://oceanlink.info

Entrepreneurial "Bat Girl" Trisha Stovel is forging her career in underwater media as co-owner of SeaProofTV with partner Russell Clark. Photo: Jill Heinerth

The Oceanlink website offer interviews with and profiles of successful marine scientists in addition to links to educational institutions that offer programs in marine careers.

Marine Advanced Technology Education Center (MATE)

www.marinetech.org

The Marine Advanced Technology Education Center website represents a national partnership of organizations working to improve marine technical education to prepare America's future workforce for ocean careers. The website includes educational links and profiles as well as scholarship and internship information, job listings and resources for employers.

Association for the Sciences of Limnology and Oceanography (ASLO)

http://www.aslo.org/career/aquaticcareer.html

The Association for the Sciences of Limnology and Oceanography (ASLO) helps students prepare for careers in aquatic science. Their website provides career resources and lists institutions offering graduate programs in limnology and oceanography.

Centers for Ocean Sciences Education Excellence (COSEE)

www.oceancareers.com

OceanCareers.com is a nationwide project supported by the Centers for Ocean Sciences Education Excellence (COSEE) California, part of an NSF network created to foster scientists' involvement in ocean science education. This site describes over fifty ocean-related careers, offers links to universities and college programs, provides connections to professional societies, lists internship opportunities and offers active job listings.

Marine Technology Society

https://www.mtsociety.org

The Marine Technology Society gives members of academia, government and industry a common forum for the exchange of information and ideas. A membership based organization, MTS boasts participation by businesses, institutions, individual professionals and students who are ocean engineers, technologists, policy makers and educators.

Hopkins Marine Station at Stanford University

http://hopkins.stanford.edu/careers.htm

This comprehensive website of the Hopkins Marine Station at Stanford University offers career seeking advice, links and job listings.

The Student Conservation Association (SCA)

https://www.thesca.org

SCA's mission is to build the next generation of conservation leaders and inspire lifelong stewardship of the environment and communities by engaging young people with hands-on environmental challenges, creating future stewards of our land and waters. They offer opportunities that range from babysitting turtle hatchlings to improving our national parks to assisting biologists and other resources managers in protection efforts.

National Marine Educators Association (NMEA)

http://marine-ed.org

National Marine Educators Association (NMEA) is a member-based organization of classroom teachers, informal educators, university professors, and scientists working together to advance the understanding and protection of our freshwater and marine ecosystems. NMEA is a national organization powered by 17 individual, regional chapters that provide the on-the-ground efforts that support and promote national initiatives in education and conservation such as Ocean Literacy.

NMEA has a 37 year history and hosts inspiring annual conferences in different locations across North America. NMEA has also recently inspired the creation of the European Marine Science Educators Association and collaborates regularly with similar associations based in Australia (MESA), Japan, and beyond.

Additional Links to Career Opportunities

The American Society of Limnology and Oceanography -- positions offered: http://aslo.org/employment.html

Aquaculture Jobs, provided by the World Aquaculture Network Information Center: http://www.aquanic.org/text/job_serv.htm

Dr. Irena Radić Rossi leads archaeological investigations of a 1st century BC ship in Pag Croatia. Work in this bay has been ongoing for ten years. Photos: Jill Heinerth

Experience.com -- career resources and online counseling, along with career descriptions and salary information: www.experience.com

Career Magazine -- information on employers, internships, job fairs, and more: http://career-mag.com

Bridges -- career website for students (middle and high school) and adults, this site offers a special section for parents, a career aptitude survey, college information, job searches, publications, and school-to-career curriculum: http://www.bridges.com

JobStar.org -- resource sections on resumes, career guides, salary information: http://jobstar.org

Mapping Your Future -- great links to career guidance and job search web sites and educational institutions; also guides for specific careers, including marine science and oceanography: http://www.mapping-your-future.org

National Science Teachers Association (NSTA) Career Center -- provides a timely link between science education professionals seeking new positions and educational institutions with vacancies: http://careers.nsta.org/

Federal Jobs -- searchable job listings within the federal government: http://www.fedworld.gov/jobs/jobsearch.html

HRS Jobs -- award-winning site offering searchable job listings within the federal government (free 7-day trial, fee for longer subscriptions): http://www.hrsjobs.com

Federal job opportunities update daily -- http://www.usajobs.opm.gov/

Job Openings -- Free job listings and search service by state. Also offers information and tips on resumes, interviews, salary information (searchable by job category and location) and other job tools: http://www.jobopenings.net

Job Hunt -- Job search site (U.S. and international listings) -- with specialized sites including science, academia and education, engineering, internships and entry level, and biotechnology, among others: http://www.job-hunt.org

Job Bank USA -- Lots of career-related information, including links to localized job searches: http://www.jobbankusa.com

Dr. Barbara amEnde applies her geology and computer skills to creating the first accurate 3D map of an underwater cave during the U.S. Deep Caving Team expedition at Wakulla Springs. Photo: Jill Heinerth

National Shellfisheries Association -- positions available for shellfish scientists and researchers: http://www.shellfish.org/recruits/open.htm

Quintessential Careers -- an industry-specific career and job hunting site (including academic, educator, and teaching jobs; agriculture, zoology and the environment; and science, space and energy), as well as career advice and college information: http://www.quintcareers.com/index.html

American Fisheries Society -- online job center including student jobs and internships: http://www.fisheries.org/html/jobs.shtml

AcdJobs.com -- links to thousands of career resources by city, state, or specialty: http://www.acdjobs.com/

Career Profiles in Diving

Sandra L.H. Carroll

Sandy began diving in 1983 when it was really a masculine sport. She was the only woman in her class. During her first open water dives in Mexico, she was asked to don a horse collar BC with a backpack which was not at all what she used in her pool training. She was asked to do a back roll off of a small panga boat wearing that unfamiliar rented equipment from a shack on the beach. Admittedly she was terrified and could have made her way easily back aboard even without a ladder or assistance because of the adrenaline! Fortunately for her, the Divemaster was sensitive to her fears and guided her by the hand throughout the dive. It was because of this action that Sandy was calmed and became hooked on SCUBA diving.

Prior to diving, Sandy was a commercial photographer and she carried this passion into her diving. Sandy earned her PADI Open Water SCUBA Instructor rating in 1986, again being the only woman in her group of 20 candidates. In 1994 Sandy earned her PADI Course Director rating and has been actively teaching throughout her career at Rick's Dive 'N Travel (Then Rick's Pro Dive 'N Ski Shop) and in the state of Arkansas.

Sandy is a very strong, confident and capable woman and still encountered a few obstacles through her career. Back in the day there were a few male "moss back" divers who wouldn't let her fill their tanks because she was a woman. The solution was to simply get one of the guys to fill. Sandy does not solve problems with drama, she truly has problem solving skills that have proven tried and true in the diving industry. She is highly gifted, has a quick wit and is completely able to hold her own enabling her to prove herself naturally to the doubtful men.

Sandy is a tall woman and has had trouble finding equipment to fit her. She has had to accept that fact and be forced into men's equipment and at that time there were no women's wetsuits available. Pantyhose were worn under the old rubber suits to help them slide on easier. As soon as women's wetsuits were available she was elated!

If there was ever a role model for good diving skills and passion for diving it is Sandy. As a leader in the diving industry she is second to none. She has an amazing way of making divers feel at ease all while building their confidence. Sandy has always set the bar high for herself, her students and the teaching staff at Rick's Dive 'N Travel where she has been employed for 28 years. Sandy has made a huge positive impact on countless people over the years. She always does her best and what she knows to be right even when no one is looking. Although she is quite humble she can't help but feel gratification when hearing "Well done" or "You've made a difference in my life" by her students, some of which have gone on to be PADI instructors as a result of her influence.

Career Related Videos and Other Resources

- Aquarium Careers. Hemdal, Jay, 2001, 144 p.ISBN No. 0-595-20151-2.

- Career as a Naturalist. Birdwell, Leslie, 2000, 20 p. (Institute for Career Research CHICAGO), ISBN No. 1-58511-371-9.

- Career Ideas for Kids Who Like Science. Reeves, Diane Lindsey, 1998, 165 p. (Checkmark Books, NY), ISBN No. 0-8160-3680-2/0-8160-3686-1.

- Careers in Oceanography. American Geophysical Union, 1986, 28 p.

- Careers in Oceanography and Marine-Related Fields. The Oceanography Society, 1995, 28 p. [Single copies available from The Oceanography Society, 4052 Timber Ridge Drive, Virginia Beach, VA 23455; (804) 464-0131]

- Education & Training Programs in Oceanography & Related Fields. Marine Technology Society, 1828 L St. NW, Suite 906, Washington, D.C., 20036; (202) 775-5966.

Jitka Jandová directs marketing, sales and exports for Finnlight, a Czech Republic manufacturer of advanced lighting technologies. Raising a family and running a business makes finding time to dive challenging these days but she is dedicated to finding a balance. Photo: Jill Heinerth

- Enhancing the Postdoctoral Experience for Scientists and Engineers: A Guide for Post-doctoral Scholars, Advisers, Institutions, Funding Organizations, and Disciplinary Societies. National Academy of Sciences, National Academy of Engineering, Institute of Medicine. 212 p: http://books.nap.edu/catalog/9831.html

- Environmental Jobs for Scientists and Engineers. Basta, Nicholas, 1992, 228 p. (John Wiley and Sons, Inc., NY), ISBN No. 0-471-54034-X/0-471-54033-1.

- Footsteps in the Ocean: Careers in Diving. Lang, Denise V., 1987, 143 p. (Loadestar Books, E.P. Dutton).

- Marine Science Careers: A Sea Grant Guide to Ocean Opportunities. Adams, S., Crago, T.I., and DeRosa, S. 2000, 32 p. (University of New Hampshire Press). ISBN 0964952920.

- Ocean Opportunities. Burtis, William S., Marine Technology Society, 1991, $3.

- Opportunities in Marine and Maritime Careers. Heitzmann, W.R., 1999, 142 p. (Rev Ed. Lincolnwood, IL: VGM Career Horizons), ISBN No. 0-8442-1833-2/0-8442-1838-3.

- Put Your Science to Work: The Take-Charge Career Guide for Scientists. Fiske, P.S. 2000. 179 pp. ISBN 0-87590-295-2. American Geophysical Union.

- Questions about Careers in Oceanography. Anderson, Aubrey L., 1993, 18 p. Available from Texas Sea Grant, 1716 Briarcrest, Suite 702, Bryan, TX 77802.

- Scientists & Engineers for the New Millennium: Renewing the Human Resource. Commission of Professionals in Science and Technology (http://www.cpst.org). Document is available as a PDF file: http://www.cpst.org/S&E.PDF.

- Student Science Opportunities. Grand, Gail L., 1994, 292 p. (John Wiley and Sons, Inc., NY), ISBN No. 0-471-31088-3.

- Vocational-Technical Marine Career Opportunities in Texas. Hollin, Dewayne, 1993, 24 p. Available from Texas Sea Grant, 1716 Briarcrest, Suite 702, Bryan, TX 77802.

- Zoological Park Careers. SeaWorld Education Department. 34 p. Contact 1-800-237-4268 or visit: http://www.seaworld.org.

- Marine Careers: The Scientist. W.R. Hall and E.A. Chajes, 1993. Delaware Sea Grant Marine Advisory Service (Available from Delaware Sea Grant Marine Advisory Service, College of Marine Studies, University of Delaware, 700 Pilottown Rd., Lewes, DE 19958).

- Careers in Marine Science. (Available from the National Aquarium in Baltimore, Dept. of Education and Interpretation, Pier 3, 501 East Pratt St., Baltimore, MD 21202-3194).

- Chase, Valerie. "I'll Do Anything to Work with Whales or Dolphins!" Current 11(1): 31-33.

- Farrington, John W. "Marine Education." Oceanus 33(3): 5-11.

- Marine/Maritime Careers. Excerpted from Opportunities in Marine and Maritime Careers by W.R. Heitzmann. (Available by writing to Dr. Ray Heitzmann, Villanova University, Villanova, PA, 19085).

- Nowell, Arthur R.M. and Charles D. Hollister. "Undergraduate and Graduate Education in Oceanography." Oceanus 33(3): 31-38.

- Planning a Career in Fish and Wildlife Management. (Free from the NJ Dept. of Environmental Protection and Energy, Div. of Fish, Game & Wildlife, CN 400, Trenton, NJ 08625-0400; (609) 292-2965).

- Rosendahl, Bruce. "Becoming an Oceanographer." Sea Frontiers 36 (May-June 1990)

- Bridging the Gap: Minorities in Marine Science. VHS or CD-ROM, Copyright 2000. Southern Association of Marine Labs (SAML), the American Society for Limnology and Oceanography (ASLO), and the National Science Foundation (NSF). (Available from Marine Science Program, P.O. Box 20467, Savannah State University, Savannah, GA 31410. Attn: Video or gillganm@savstate.edu).

- Careers in Marine Science: A Diversity of Opportunities. VHS, 1995. Produced by the National Association of Marine Laboratories (NAML). $12.95. (Send order to Harbor Branch Oceanographic Institution, 5600 U.S. 1 North, Fort Pierce, FL 34946, Attn. A-V Department).

- Marine Careers. VHS, 1992. University of Delaware Sea Grant Marine Advisory Service. (Available for purchase [$15] or rental [$5 plus $25 refundable deposit]. Send check payable to "University of Delaware" with request to the Marine Communications Office, University of Delaware, Newark, DE 19716, or call (302) 831-8083 for more information).

- Ocean Exploration. VHS, 15 min. 1992. Features approximately 100 interviews with professionals, technicians, researchers, designers, and others. Produced by Full Perspective Video Services, Inc. (Available from the Eisenhower National Clearinghouse [ENC], 1929 Kenny Road, Columbus, OH 43210-1079 [ENC #: ENC-005643].

Women Mentors

Rosemary E. Lunn - Dive Industry Marketing Expert/Fixer

Advice for new women in the industry

Dive Industry Fixer, Rosemary E. Lunn (Roz) is the Business Development Director at The Underwater Marketing Company. This British firm specializes in providing marketing, communications, social media and event management for the Recreational and Technical Diving Industry.

Born in Essex, England Rosemary learned to dive in 1992 and spent every moment she could exploring Britain's magnificent coastal waters. By 1997 she'd become a PADI Instructor and taught for a season in Turkey before turning her hand to diving journalism. She has worked on History Channel and National Geographic documentaries, modeled underwater for training agency shoots, acted as a television production safety diver, opened and managed a dive center and SCUBA relayed the English Channel for charity.

Photo: Karl Shreeves

In Sept 2003 Roz worked on Carl Spencer's HMHS Britannic expedition and realized the industry needed specialist support. Thus, The Underwater Marketing Company (TUMC) was born. Roz teamed up again with Carl Spencer (and Leigh Bishop) in 2008 when the three founded and organized EUROTEK.08. She has subsequently co-organized numerous other diving shows including Rebreather Forum 3 and TEKDiveUSA. She offers wisdom from her years of diving experience.

Be yourself, you don't need to be a woman acting as a man. Whilst we all swear a bit, having a foul mouth is not that attractive in anyone.

Don't ever be scared to ask for help when you need it. But please do not play 'the girl card" or "I am a poor little female." No one appreciates that attitude. If someone is kindly carrying your twinset or rebreather down a steep dock wall and getting your rig onto the boat for you, you are more than capable of sherpa-ing their thermal protection and other ancillary equipment. Help others, so that when you need assistance, others are more than happy to support you. Conversely if you stand there saying "I can manage," when quite clearly you are struggling, have the good sense to accept help with a gracious manner. No one is patronizing you or believe you to be inadequate. They see a diver having physical issues with equipment. And never forget to say "thank you."

If you are looking at breaking into the industry, what other things do you bring to the party? Expeditions and trips can be hard enough for a team, without having to also carry

Rosemary Lunn and Dr Neal W Pollock (Research Director at Divers Alert Network). Roz and Neal were part of the organizational team that pulled together Rebreather Forum 3 held in May 2012. Photo: Roz and Neal photographed at Divetech's Inner Space. Courtesy of The Underwater Marketing Company

a lazy member who does not pull their weight. We all dive, so what makes you a useful person to have around? Do you speak a foreign language and are you a good negotiator? Having a diplomat that can speak more than one language is an asset for any company. Can you sew? It is a handy skill for fixing torn clothing or damaged equipment. Everyone needs accurate gas in their cylinders - are you willing and able to blend gas at anti-social hours? An army marches on its stomach and so do divers. Can you cook a filling and scrumptious meal for 12 people? Do you know a Phillips screwdriver from a Flathead? Sometimes the most useful thing you can do is hand an engineer tools on demand, whilst shining a light on the broken equipment. (This generally happens at night in the pouring rain, so can you do this cheerfully too?) Being an instructor doesn't mean you just swan in at the start of the class and teach, and swish out when class finishes. You have many responsibilities to your employer if you are a dive pro. What are your sales techniques like? Do you have the backup knowledge to give honest experienced advice about training or equipment? Remember making tea or coffee is never beneath you.

There will be times where people criticize your work. Listen to what they may say, and think about why they say it. Some of it will be constructive, some won't. Unfortunately we are all human, so it is probable it will all hurt. Take notice of the useful advice and grow a thick skin. You are being critiqued because someone cares and is taking time to help you develop and reach your potential, or because someone is threatened by your performance and abilities. Learn to recognize the difference.

Your instructor is not there to be your new best friend, they are there to train you to be the best diver you can be. I hated the guts of the instructor who taught my Divemaster course. And I have forgotten how many times I have silently thanked my lucky stars that I had Stuart Douglas teach me how to be a decent Divemaster.

Remember nothing is forever, i.e. if you are gibbering with cold, you will soon be warm again. And when you are surrounded by dolphins, take a moment to drink in and appreciate the wonder of this special interaction.

Diving has the ability to build friendships that bind you together as strong as hoops of steel, no matter where the respective parties are in the world. The industry is a small one with numerous connections. Whether you like it or not, your reputation will go before you.

There is nothing wrong with ambition, just don't trample on other people's dreams or steal their ideas as you strive for the top.

Roz can be reached at: roz@tumc.co.uk

Social Resources

There are numerous social and online organizations available that can act as your "tribe," your mentors and sisters of the sea.

The Women Divers Hall of Fame (WDHOF)

www.wdhof.org

The Women Divers Hall of Fame (WDHOF) is a 501(c)3 nonprofit organization dedicated to honoring and raising awareness of the contributions of outstanding women divers. WDHOF provides educational, mentorship, financial, and career opportunities to the diving community throughout the world. Each year, WDHOF awards scholarships and training grants that provide financial and educational support to individuals of all ages, particularly those who are preparing for professional careers that involve diving.

The inaugural class of the Women Divers Hall of Fame celebrating at the Beneath the Sea Show in 2000. Since that time, the group has grown exponentially and matured into a remarkable service organization that offers scholarships and mentoring for women around the world. Photo: Alese Pechter

WDHOF Members are the pioneers, leaders, innovators and world record holders throughout the international diving community. These areas of diving and undersea endeavors include: the arts, science, medicine, exploration and technology, marine archeology, business, media, training and education, safety, commercial and military diving, free diving, and other underwater sports. Members are selected and invited to join the organization on an annual basis.

Each year, the members of WDHOF attend various consumer diving expositions, the DEMA show, as well as symposia, conferences, seminars and special events throughout the United States. These venues allow members the opportunity to give presentations/seminars about their areas of expertise and speak directly with the public.

The members of WDHOF are an elite group that includes the most notable women leaders and innovators in the diving community. It became the goal of its founders to recognize and honor, while raising public awareness of these women's exceptional contributions and supporting the next generation of women divers.

WDHOF scholarship and internship offerings are detailed later in this chapter.

The South Florida Women Divers

http://www.sfwd.net

The South Florida Women Divers (SFWD) is a women-only SCUBA diving club serving Palm Beach and Broward Counties including the communities of West Palm Beach, Boynton Beach, Highland Beach, Delray Beach, Boca Raton, Deerfield Beach, Hillsboro

Beach, Coral Springs, Coconut Creek, Margate, North Lauderdale, Parkland, Tamarac, Pompano Beach, Fort Lauderdale, and beyond.

Over 80 women, aged 14-79, are members of SFWD, which was launched in 1991. Members are single, married, mothers, grandmothers, newly certified divers and instructors with thousands of dives. They even include associate members who do not dive. They dive together locally and also take international trips together, invite inspirational speakers and raise money to support important causes.

Society of Lady Divers

http://SocietyofLadyDivers.com

The Society of Lady Divers is an organization of women around the world who share a passion for SCUBA diving. They generate education and inspiration for diving and ocean awareness by traveling together, sharing adventures with others and setting an example for a growing community of SCUBA divers. From tips on dive gear to best dive destinations, the Society of Lady Divers is a great community of ocean enthusiasts who aspire to make a difference. Membership is free and includes a well produce Internet zine.

Stay connected by following along in their forum or enjoy articles in their blog. Among many other exciting things to come, Society of Lady Divers offers a sense of unity for divers and ocean enthusiasts around the globe. Join them in a community of passion for all things ocean!

SCUBA Diver Girls

http://SCUBAdivergirls.com

SCUBA Diver Girls began as a Facebook group of women in the San Diego region and has grown to include shopping opportunities, mentoring, training links and travel.

Dive Bunnies

www.divebunnies.com

Dive Bunnies was started by a group of women working in Egypt. Their blog keeps visitors up to date on political issues in Egypt, animal life on the reefs of Sharm el Sheikh and successes of women divers. They even post a Dive Divas Hall of Fame.

Miss Scuba

www.miss-scuba.com

Miss Scuba was designed to bring women together from all over the world who share enthusiasm about diving, travel and adventure. Miss Scuba provides travel opportunities, helpful tips new product information and jewelry sales. They are represented by women from 20 countries all over the world.

Scholarships for Women

Women Divers Hall of Fame Scholarships

The Women Divers Hall of Fame offers scholarships in conservation, marine biology, underwater archaeology, and journalism, graphic arts and photography. They are intended to support tuition and fees, independent research, and/or an internship program at an accredited university. Scholarships are paid directly to the recipient. The following scholarships were current at the time of printing, but the program is expanding annually.

Applicants may apply for one scholarship per year via an online form. If you have questions after you've carefully read the application instructions, please email: scholarships@wdhof.org. The deadline for receipt of applications is usually sometime in November with notification in February each year. The following list represents the awards available for presentation in 2015. Check www.wdhof.org for details and current listings.

WDHOF SCHOLARSHIP IN MARINE OR UNDERWATER EDUCATION

A $2,000 scholarship will be awarded to a qualified woman of any age to plan and conduct an education project in marine or underwater STEM programs for students in grades K-12. The scholarship may also be used to support independent research by an educator in any underwater STEM area. Applicants should hold a degree (or equivalent certificate) in education, museum studies, or other relevant area, and have experience teaching marine science, technology, or engineering at any K-12 level.

WDHOF/LIFEGUARD SYSTEMS PUBLIC SAFETY DIVING SCHOLARSHIP

A scholarship to take an unlimited number of any Lifeguard Systems open, Levels 1-3, public safety and water rescue certification training programs for a duration of one year will be awarded to a woman 18 years of age or older, with a commitment to public safety diving and water rescue, and preferably some experience in public safety (e.g., EMT certification, volunteer firefighter, in law enforcement, forensics, etc.). The awardee might be able to stay in the host's facility (e.g., fire department) at no cost, if such an option is available. Applicants must be certified to dive, have their own dive gear, and must be capable of getting to and from the training programs. The recipient will most likely also be able to take additional training programs from at least one other water rescue/recovery training agency.

WDHOF / AGGRESSOR AND DANCER FLEET GRADUATE SCHOLARSHIP IN MARINE CONSERVATION

A $2,000 scholarship will be awarded to a qualified woman of any age who is enrolled in an accredited graduate academic or research program in the field of marine conservation. The scholarship is intended to assist with college tuition/fees or may be used to support independent research or an internship program at an accredited university.

WDHOF / CECELIA CONNELLY MEMORIAL GRADUATE SCHOLARSHIP IN UNDERWATER ARCHAEOLOGY, sponsored by the Connelly family

A $2,000 scholarship will be awarded to a deserving woman graduate student. Applicants must be enrolled in an accredited course of study in the field of underwater archaeology. The scholarship is intended to assist with college tuition/fees or field study costs and is open to candidates worldwide. A GPA of 3.0 or better is required, and the applicant must be in good standing with her academic institution. First year graduate students may submit verification of a minimum overall GPA of 2.5 from their final year as an undergraduate. There is no applicant age limit.

WDHOF / CECELIA CONNELLY MEMORIAL UNDERGRADUATE SCHOLARSHIP IN UNDERWATER ARCHAEOLOGY, sponsored by the Connelly family

A $750 scholarship will be awarded to a deserving woman undergraduate student. Applicants must be enrolled in an accredited course of study in the field of underwater archaeology. The scholarship is intended to assist with college tuition/fees or field study costs and is open to candidates worldwide. An overall GPA of 2.5 or better is required and the applicant must be in good standing with her academic institution. There is no applicant age limit.

WDHOF / ELIZABETH GREENHALGH MEMORIAL SCHOLARSHIP IN JOURNALISM, GRAPHIC ARTS, OR PHOTOGRAPHY, sponsored by Deb Greenhalgh

A $1,500 scholarship will be awarded to a woman diver who is furthering her education beyond high school in the field of journalism, graphic arts, or photography to better serve the ocean environment or ocean community. The scholarship is intended to assist with college tuition/fees or may be used to support an internship program at an accredited university.

WDHOF UNDERGRADUATE MARINE RESEARCH INTERNSHIP IN MARINE BIOLOGY, sponsored by Sue Morra, Ph.D. and Kathleen Dudzinski, Ph.D.

A $1,000 scholarship will be awarded to a woman UNDERGRADUATE student who is (or will be) participating in an internship program with a focus in marine biology. Students must have completed at least 60 credits or hold third year (junior) status prior to starting the internship.

WDHOF UNDERGRADUATE SCHOLARSHIP IN MARINE CONSERVATION, sponsored by Sherry A. Reed

A $1,000 scholarship will be awarded to a deserving UNDERGRADUATE woman who is enrolled in an accredited academic or research program in the field of marine conservation. Special consideration will be given to those women who are scuba certified. The scholarship is intended to assist with college tuition/fees or may be used to support independent research or an internship program at an accredited university.

Women Divers Hall of Fame Training Grants

WDHOF ADVANCED DIVE TRAINING GRANT sponsored by Bonnie Toth

A $1,000 training grant (up to $500 for training and up to $500 for dive equipment) will be awarded to a deserving woman diver of any age and background who wishes to further her dive education through an approved scuba diving program beyond the basic certification level.

WDHOF / AMELIA BEHRENS-FURNISS MEMORIAL HARDHAT TRAINING GRANT

A $1,000 grant will be awarded to a deserving woman diver of any age and background who wishes to begin or further her training in hardhat diving through an approved hardhat dive training program.

WDHOF / CODE BLUE EDUCATION LTD DIVER MEDIC TRAINING GRANT

A $2000.00 training grant ($1275.00 for training and up to $725.00 for food and accommodations) will be awarded to a deserving male or female who wishes to further his/her diving training/education as a diver medic technician. The recipient must enroll in an approved Diver Medic Training facility with Code Blue Education Ltd in the United Kingdom.

WDHOF / ELLA JEAN MORGAN MEMORIAL DIVE TRAINING GRANT

A $1,000 training grant will be awarded to a deserving young female, age 15-21, who wishes to begin her dive education/training. Up to $500 may be used for dive training, and up to $500 may be used for dive equipment.

WDHOF / HUGH FLETCHER MEMORIAL TRAINING GRANT TO ASSIST THE DISABLED TO DIVE

A $1,000 training grant (up to $500 for training and up to $500 for dive equipment) will be awarded to any disabled diver who wishes to pursue or further his/her dive education and purchase adaptive equipment, or to a divemaster, assistant instructor, or instructor to gain the required education/training to assist or teach the disabled to dive. Candidates can be male or female.

WDHOF / KIDS SEA CAMP BASIC DIVE TRAINING GRANTS, sponsored by Margo Peyton

Two $500 training grants will be awarded to deserving women divers of any age and background who wish to begin their dive education through a PADI scuba certification course. Two awards will be given to novice divers to gain the fundamental knowledge, skills and ability to safely breathe underwater.

WDHOF / MORGAN/O'NEILL UNDERWATER PHOTOGRAPHY GRANT

A $2,000 grant will be awarded to a qualified female photographer of any age to continue her professional development in the field of underwater photography. Applicants must be certified divers with significant dive experience. The successful applicant will be a serious, career-minded woman with the intent to (continue to) develop her career in underwater photography.

WDHOF / OCEAN PALS JUNIOR DIVE TRAINING GRANT

A $1,000 training grant (up to $500 for training and up to $500 for dive equipment) will be awarded to a deserving young woman, ages 13-16, who wishes to begin or further her dive education/training. Up to $500 may be used for dive training, and up to $500 may be used for dive equipment.

WDHOF / SCUBA MADE EASY TRAINING GRANT IN MARINE SCIENCE, OCEANOGRAPHY OR OCEAN ENGINEERING

A $1,000 training grant (up to $500 for training and up to $500 for dive equipment) will be awarded to a deserving woman diver of any age, working in the areas of marine science, oceanography or ocean engineering. The training grant is to be used for the purpose of continuing diver education/training and is open to candidates worldwide.

WDHOF / WOMEN'S SCUBA ASSOCIATION TRAINING GRANT sponsored by Jennifer King

A $750 training grant (up to $500 for training and up to $250 for dive equipment) will be awarded to a deserving young male or female who wishes to begin or further his/her dive education/training. Candidates must be enrolled in an ROTC or JROTC program, military academy or be a Sea Cadet.

The Rolex Our World-Underwater Internships

NORTH AMERICA INTERNSHIP

The Rolex Our World-Underwater Scholarship Society offers summer internships in North America for 1-3 month periods to college undergraduates and graduating high school seniors. Internship recipients receive a grant to help fund travel to/from site, room and board, and a stipend to cover living expenses. The current North American internship sponsors include the REEF Environmental Education Foundation, American Academy of Underwater Sciences (AAUS), National Park Service, "Sport Diver" Magazine and Monterey Bay Aquarium. Several are awarded annually.

EUROPEAN YOUNG PHOTOGRAPHER INTERNSHIP

The European Young Photographer Internship provides an opportunity for a promising young photographer to further develop skills and experience by working alongside an already accomplished underwater photographer. This internship is awarded to the winning entrant at a competition held during the International Festival of Underwater Film in Marseilles, France.

For more information contact: Roberta Flanders, Executive Administrator
execadmin@owuscholarship.org

The Rolex Our World Underwater Scholarships

http://www.owuscholarship.org

For more than 35 years, the Our World-Underwater Scholarship Society has provided firsthand experiences in underwater-related disciplines to young people considering careers in the underwater world. Each year, a scholar is selected from North America, Europe, and Australasia to work with leaders in marine-related fields partaking in endeavors ranging from scientific expeditions, underwater research, field study, laboratory assignments, equipment testing and design, photographic instruction, and/or other specialized assignments. Scholars spend a year traveling extensively to gain exposure and get hands-on experiences in activities that will contribute to a well-rounded education.

Each Rolex Scholar is granted a coordinator who assists in organizing his or her itinerary. Breadth of experience is emphasized, but each program is tailored to meet each scholar's background and interests. Itineraries may include time with specialists in such areas as biology, archaeology, dive industry-related operations, underwater photography, and conservation. Other areas of study may include: hyperbaric medicine, equipment design and manufacturing, education, dive management, marine expeditions, government/policy, tourism, publishing. media, commercial diving, scientific research, and ecological activism.

The global underwater community views the Rolex Scholars as having the potential to make significant contributions to the underwater world even though they may not have yet chosen a specific career path. Exposure to a wide array of topics and work environments provides the scholars with a broad overview of the underwater world that will help guide career decisions.

Each Rolex Scholarship provides a hands-on introduction to underwater and other aquatic-related endeavors for a young person considering a career in an underwater-related discipline. One scholar is selected from each of the three regions and each scholar spends approximately one year working side by side with current leaders in underwater fields. Each scholar travels primarily within his or her region, but may have opportunities throughout the underwater world. The range of experiences may include active participation in field studies, underwater research, scientific expeditions, laboratory assignments, equipment testing and design, photographic instruction, and other specialized assignments.

Scholars pursue activities in their chosen disciplines during the one-year period between Our World Underwater Scholarship Society annual spring meetings. Experiences may last from a few days to over a month. At the conclusion of each experience, the scholar moves on to another, so the scholarship year involves extensive travel. The scholar is literally on the road from spring-to-spring with very little time at a home base. Scholars spend most of the year with the Society's friends, hosts and coordinators around the world. The experiences vary from year to year depending upon the scholar's interests and the availability of expeditions and hosts' opportunities. These experiences make up the real heart of the scholarship. The opportunity to join a host's daily activities exposes the scholar to the realities of the host's special pursuits.

The maximum cash amount for the North American Rolex Scholarship is $25,000, for the European Rolex Scholarship the amount is £16,000 and for the Australasian Scholarship Aus $30,000.

Our World-Underwater Scholarship Society funds are used for transportation and living expenses. The North American and European Rolex Scholars must submit a complete accounting for all expenditures. Logs, journals, financial reports, and other communications are mandatory and must be submitted monthly to the Scholarship Society for review by the Board of Directors and the Executive Committee.

Women Mentors

Robin MacFadden Parish, Women Divers Hall of Fame 2012

For many years Robin has served as the National Coordinator of the Rolex Scholarship of the Our World-Underwater Scholarship Society (OWUSS). She connects young people with the world's experts in conservation, underwater photography, exploration, and marine technology. She has been diving since 1970 and an instructor since 1976. Robin was the first female recipient of the Rolex Scholarship, and went on to a career in marine biology, working in environmental consulting, researching crustacean behavioral ecology, and doing groundwork for the creation of marine sanctuaries. As VP of North American Operations and a member of the Board of Directors of OWUSS, she has been instrumental in the orga-

Robin Parish and Jill Heinerth at the Boston Sea Rovers Show.

nization's global expansion and establishing internships. An educator, speaker, and passionate advocate for marine conservation, Robin encourages young people of all ages to learn about the sea and become part of the key to its future.

The Georgia Williams Youth Diving Scholarship

www.immersediving.com

Georgia Williams suddenly and unexpectedly lost her life at the end of May 2013. Her spirit has touched people all over the world. Georgia Williams lived life with an adventurous, outgoing attitude. She loved being outdoors and being active. Number three on Georgia's wish list in life was to go scuba diving.

The Georgia Williams Trust formed in Georgia's memory aims to enable young people to participate in life-building adventurous and outdoor activities, and to contribute to the local community.

The Georgia Williams Diving Scholarship is an opportunity for one young person to pursue an interest in the underwater world, and in turn to enable other young people to have access to scuba diving activities. The annual Scholarship is jointly funded by The Georgia Williams Trust and Immerse School of Diving, and sponsored by the incredible family team at Otter Watersports Drysuits.

The Georgia Williams Diving Scholar learns to become a fully qualified scuba diver and trains to attain PADI (Junior) Master Scuba Diver rating with Immerse School of Diving in Telford, England. Over the course of the year the Scholar undertakes the PADI Open Water, PADI (Junior) Advanced Open Water, Emergency First Response CPR and First Aid, PADI (Junior) Rescue Diver, and five PADI Specialty diving courses. The Scholar is able to attend the Club Immerse weekly pool sessions to develop their diving skills and experience, and also has the opportunity to complete at least fifty scuba dives over the course of the year with Immerse School of Diving.

In addition, the Scholar has the chance to experience a range of scuba diving experiences. The experiences differ depending on the opportunities presented during the Scholarship year, and the Scholar's personal interests. They may include underwater scientific research, environmental activities, photography and videography, and diving journalism. At the end of the Scholarship the Scholar has all the qualifications and experience required to commence training to become a PADI professional diver when they turn eighteen, opening up the opportunity to pursue a career in the scuba diving industry.

American Academy of Underwater Scientists Internships

http://www.aaus.org/aausowuss_internship

The Our World-Underwater Scholarship has collaborated with the American Academy of Underwater Sciences to create a new scientific diving internship. This internship will provide undergraduates with the experience and opportunities necessary for a future in science, diving for research, or scientific diving-related fields. Intern applicants can be students from colleges and universities with an interest in science and diving. The program runs primarily from mid-May through August and will include training at one of several AAUS organizational member sites. This training will give the intern the necessary dive qualifications to allow participation on research projects requiring scientific diving and introduce the intern to careers that utilize scientific diving as a tool. Once trained as an AAUS-recognized diver-in training, interns will participate in underwater field-work at one or more locations and research facilities associated with AAUS. The internship will be supported by funding for travel to/from site, room, board, and other internship-related expenses.

Boston Sea Rovers Summer Internships

www.bostonsearovers.com

The Boston Sea Rovers offers internships to qualified graduating high school seniors, college freshmen and sophomores interested in pursuing underwater careers. Immediately following graduation or the spring semester, the scholar will intern with members of the Boston Sea Rovers and associates located throughout the United States to experience a wide variety of jobs and career choices. Based in part on the personal interests of the scholar, the Internship provides advanced dive training courses and ample opportunities to dive and train with a variety of professionals in a

Each year, a growing class of Sea Rovers meet at their Annual Clinic; the oldest dive show in the U.S.

broad cross section of diving environments. Opportunities will include hands-on work with professional under water photographers and filmmakers, educational specialists, marine engineers and scientists, equipment manufacturer's representatives, and dive shop owners.

In addition to the unique time spent with distinguished members, the Sea Rover Intern will be outfitted with dive equipment (provided by Sea Rover Clinic corporate sponsors) for their use throughout the summer and will receive the necessary financial support to ensure travel and living expenses.

At-Sea Opportunities for College Students

The Marine Advanced Technology Education (MATE) Center has developed the At-Sea Technical Internship Program. Interns work as marine technicians aboard sea-going research vessels that are part of the University National Oceanographic Laboratory System (UNOLS), the United States Coast Guard, and the Ocean Exploration Trust. Email: tlunsford@marinetech.org.

State Internships

CONNECTICUT

http://www.ct.gov/deep/cwp/view.asp?a=2688&q=322346

Recognizing the need to provide hands-on work experience not typically available to students in the traditional academic setting, the Connecticut Department of Energy and Environmental Protection has established an internship program to acquaint students with DEEP's mission. Our internship program allows qualified students to obtain academic credit from their institution, while also gaining valuable experience in the workforce. Attracting and retaining top-notch employees is crucial to the success of the DEEP. To foster both their personal and professional growth, interns are afforded an opportunity to familiarize themselves with hands-on work of the Agency, such as research, monitoring, enforcement, environmental clean-up, community involvement, and prevention.

NEW YORK

http://www.dec.ny.gov/about/34336.html

The Department of Environmental Conservation participates in the New York Leaders Student Intern Program. The single centralized portal supports established internship programs and existing relationships with colleges and universities by providing a single resource to which schools may direct students as well as a centralized place for DEC to post new, unpaid internship opportunities. The program provides talented undergraduate or graduate students who are New York State residents or who attend a New York State college, university or graduate program and are interested in exploring a career in public service. Student interns will be given the opportunity to gain on-the-job training to enhance and supplement their academic course work.

NEW JERSEY

http://www.nj.gov/dep/jobs/

New marine oriented internship opportunities are posted frequently at the link above.

http://www.state.nj.us/dep/wms/bear/recruit.htm

The AmeriCorps New Jersey Watershed Ambassadors Program is an environmental community service program administered by the New Jersey Department of Environmental Protection to raise public awareness about water and watershed issues and to promote watershed stewardship through direct community involvement. The program works to improve water quality by exploring relationships between people and the environment, nurturing community-based environmental activities, and empowering residents to make responsible and informed decisions regarding their watershed.

Every year, the AmeriCorps New Jersey Watershed Ambassadors Program places twenty new AmeriCorps members with host agencies in each of New Jersey's twenty Watershed Management Areas to serve as "Watershed Ambassadors" to their watershed communities. Over the course of 1700 hours, these ambassadors learn from Department staff and then train local volunteers to monitor the waters in their community using state and federally-approved visual and biological monitoring techniques.

Additional Links to Internships and Volunteer Opportunities

American Association for the Advancement of Science (AAAS) Fellowships for Scientists and Engineers: http://fellowships.aaas.org

AAAS Guide to Graduate Education in Science, Engineering, and Public Policy: http://www.aaas.org/spp/sepp/sepfaq.htm

American Fisheries Society Student Opportunities and Internships: http://www.fisheries.org/html/jobs.shtml

American Society of Limnology and Oceanography (ASLO) Aquatic Science Career Information: http://www.aslo.org/students/studentops.html

Career Services Network of Syracuse University: http://careers.syr.edu/internships.htm

The Environmental Careers Organization (ECO) helps students and graduates find paid internships in the U.S. and abroad. They also sponsor career fairs, conferences, and publications: http://eco.org

American Zoo and Aquarium Association (type "intern" into search box to see a listing of internships): http://aza.org/joblistings/index.cfm

Environmental Protection Agency Graduate Fellowships: http://es.epa.gov/ncerqa/fellow

K-Adult Opportunities Listings from The Bridge: http://www.vims.edu/bridge/summer.html

Listing of Paid Internships Maintained by the Environmental Careers Organization: http://www.eco.org/career/available.htm

Marine Science-Related Professional Societies (a list compiled by the Marine Technology Society): http://www.mtsociety.org/education/otherlinks.cfm

National Academies Careers and Fellowships Information: http://www.nationalacademies.org/careerguides.html

National Institutes of Health (NIH) Student Training Opportunities: www.training.nih.gov

National Oceanic and Atmospheric Administration (NOAA) Internships, Fellowships & Grants: http://www.rdc.noaa.gov/~hrmo/jobs.htm

National Oceanic and Atmospheric Administration (NOAA) Fisheries Office for Law Enforcement: http://www.nmfs.noaa.gov/ole/about/hq_internship.html

National Park Service Career and Internship Information: http://www.nps.gov/personnel

National Science Foundation's Student Opportunities Listings: http://www.nsf.gov/about/career_opps/careers/student.jsp

National Sea Grant College Program Fellowship Opportunities: http://www.seagrant.noaa.gov/funding/knauss/knauss.html

National Wildlife Federation Internship Opportunities: http://www.nwf.org/careergateway/internships.cfm

Smithsonian Environmental Research Center Internships: http://www.serc.si.edu/pro_-training/internships/internships.jsp

Smithsonian Institution Internships: http://www.intern.si.edu/

Student Opportunities from The Bridge: http://www.vims.edu/bridge/student_opp.html

U.S. Department of Commerce's Student Employment Opportunities: http://ohrm.os.doc.-gov/Career/DEV01_000328

Links to Marine Science Related Schools

U.S. News and World Report's searchable college database: www.usnews.com/usnews/edu/college/cosearch.htm

College searches by CollegeNet: http://cnsearch.collegenet.com/cgi-bin/CN/index

Searchable Database of career offerings at colleges, universities, and vocational schools: http://www.overview.com/colleges

Listing of colleges and universities in the U.S. and Canada with curricula in the atmospheric, oceanic, hydrologic, and related sciences (maintained by the American Meteorological Society): http://www.ametsoc.org/curricula/index.html

The Princeton Review -- Information about colleges, careers, financial aid, and lots more: http://www.princetonreview.com/home.asp

Academic Programs in Aquatic Science: http://www.aslo.org/career.html

Do you want to learn more about women mentors and diving careers? Visit The Women Divers Hall of Fame resources online at www.WDHOF.org. You'll find drysuit guru Susan Long, the CEO of DUI and Rear Admirals Martha Herb and Bette Bolivar who are making history in the Navy. You can read about other luminaries like Norine Rouse who was the first women hired by UNEXCO in the sixties and Zale Parry, the damsel in distress from the early Sea Hunt films. You will find maritime archaeologists, shark researchers, conservationists, photographers, professional athletes and world record holders. You can also read about the successful recipients of WDHOF Scholarships and Training Grants. You can learn more about Christie Wilcox, a Ph.D. Candidate in the Cell and Molecular Biology program at the University of Hawaii, and UC Davis Divemaster and California Department of Fish and Wildlife (CDFW) scientific diver, Athena Maguire who is aspiring to be an environmental fisheries scientist in a management role or Danielle Carr, a Ph.D. candidate who is focused on ways to describe how climate change and other human stressors affect coral reef communities.

The Women Divers Hall of Fame has helped to bring these remarkable women into the limelight where we can celebrate their accomplishments and contributions to the diving industry. There are several books left to write about their collective work and wisdom and we wish we could have included all these special people in this volume!

Continue to follow our blog at WomenUnderwater.com where we share new insights into equipment and further stories about women who have left their mark in diving.

Made in the USA
Middletown, DE
20 February 2021